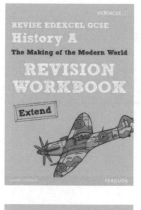

edexcel

REVISE EDEXCEL GCSE
History
Specification A Modern World History
REVISION WORKBOOK
Extend

Author: Steve Waugh

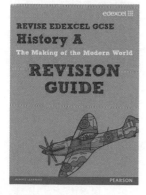

THE REVISE EDEXCEL SERIES
Available in print or online

Online editions for all titles in the Revise Edexcel series are available Autumn 2012.

Presented on our ActiveLearn platform, you can view the full book and customise it by adding notes, comments and weblinks.

Print editions

History A Extend Revision Workbook	9781446905036
History A Support Revision Workbook	9781446905050
History A Revision Guide	9781446905128

Online editions

History A Extend Revision Workbook	9781446905012
History A Support Revision Workbook	9781446904978
History A Revision Guide	9781446905029

Print and online editions are also available for History Specification B Support and Extend Workbooks and Revision Guide.

This Revision Workbook is designed to complement your classroom and home learning, and to help you prepare for the exam. It does not include all the content and skills needed for the complete course. It is designed to work in combination with Edexcel's main GCSE History 2009/2012 Series.

To find out more visit:
www.pearsonschools.co.uk/edexcelgcsehistoryrevision

ALWAYS LEARNING

PEARSON

About this book

This workbook has been written to help you practise your exam skills as you prepare for your GCSE History exams for Unit 1, Unit 2 and Unit 3. You'll find practice for each question type in each unit, helping you to understand what is required. You'll find answers to the activities at the back of the book, so that you can check whether you're on track after you've completed the activities.

Unit 1: Peace and War: International Relations, 1900-91

There are six sections in Unit 1, but you must answer questions on only **three** sections. In this workbook, the Unit 1 questions have been colour-coded to help you quickly find the ones relevant to you. In the exam, though, you'll need to make sure you know which sections you've studied so that you can go straight to them and not waste time looking at questions for other sections.

In each section, you need to answer three questions: you answer nine questions in total. You'll find guidance on each of these question types on pages 1–18. Note that you have a choice of questions in (b).

Question (a)	2 marks	Pages 1–6
Question (b)(i) or Question (b)(ii)	6 marks	Pages 6–11
Question (c)	12 marks	Pages 11–18

Unit 2: Modern World Depth Study

This workbook covers the following three options in Unit 2.
- 2A: Germany 1918–39 (pages 26–44)
- 2B: Russia 1917–39 (pages 45–63)
- 2C: The USA 1919–41 (pages 64–82)

You will have studied one of these options and the exam paper for Unit 2 will only have questions for your option, but note that you have a choice of question in question 2 and in question 3. You answer six questions.

Question 1(a)	4 marks	Page 20	Question 2(a) or Question 2(b)	8 marks plus 3 marks for spelling, punctuation and grammar	Page 24
Question 1(b)	6 marks	Page 21	Question 3(a) or Question 3(b)	16 marks plus 4 marks for spelling, punctuation and grammar	Page 25
Question 1(c)	8 marks	Page 22			
Question 1(d)	8 marks	Page 23			

Unit 3: Modern World Source Enquiry

This workbook covers the three options in Unit 3.
- 3A: War and the transformation of British society, c.1903–28 (pages 92–104)
- 3B: War and the transformation of British society, c.1931–51 (pages 105–117)
- 3C: A divided union? The USA 1945–70 (pages 118–130)

You will have studied one of these options and the exam paper for Unit 3 will only have questions for your option. You answer all five questions in the exam paper.

Question 1	6 marks	Page 87	Question 4	10 marks	Page 90
Question 2	8 marks	Page 88	Question 5	16 marks plus 4 marks for spelling, punctuation and grammar	Page 91
Question 3	10 marks	Page 89			

Unit 1: Peace and War: International Relations, 1900–91

Introduction

The Unit 1 exam paper

Unit 1 investigates different periods in international relations. These are divided into six sections. The six sections are:

- Section 1: Why did the war break out? International rivalry 1900–14
- Section 2: The peace settlement: 1918–28
- Section 3: Why did war break out? International relations 1929–39
- Section 4: How did the Cold War develop? 1943–56
- Section 5: Three Cold War crises: Berlin, Cuba and Czechoslovakia c.1957–69
- Section 6: Why did the Cold War end? The invasion of Afghanistan (1979) to the collapse of the Soviet Union (1991)

You will be studying **three** of these sections. Make sure you know which three sections you've studied in class so that you answer the right questions.

The Unit 1 exam questions

In each section there are three different styles of questions: part (a) , part (b) and part (c).

- Part (a) questions are describe questions, worth 2 marks. See pages 1–6.
- Part (b) questions are key features questions, worth 6 marks. See pages 6–11.
- Part (c) questions are causation questions, worth 12 marks. See pages 11–18.

Answering part (a) questions

Part (a) is a describe question, for example:

Describe one reason why Austria-Hungary seized Bosnia in 1908. (2)

- This is worth 2 marks.
- It could ask you to describe one feature of an event including a cause, action, aim, way, decision, reaction, consequence or challenge.
- To get full marks, you have to identify one factor and give a brief description of it.

This question is marked in two levels as shown in the mark scheme below.

Level	Mark	Descriptor
1	1	**Simple statement(s)** These are often very brief and/or generalised, for example: Austria-Hungary seized Bosnia in 1908.
2	2	**Developed statement** This is a simple statement with supporting material. Using the word 'because' often means that the statement has been supported. Austria-Hungary seized Bosnia in 1908 because of fears that Serbia would seize the province first. Austria was frightened of Serbian nationalism.

Activity 1: Understanding the exam question

Part (a) questions are worth 2 marks.

1. Approximately how long would you expect your answer to be? Ring your choice.
    - Two sentences
    - A paragraph
    - Two or three paragraphs

2. Approximately how long should you spend answering this question? Ring your choice.
    - 1 minute
    - 3 minutes
    - 10 minutes

3. Choose the three questions below for the three sections you are studying.

    ☐ Section 1: *Describe **one** reason why Austria-Hungary seized Bosnia in 1908. (2)*

    ☐ Section 2: *Describe **one** decision which was made about Turkey at the Treaty of Sèvres. (2)*

    ☐ Section 3: *Describe **one** reason why Hitler introduced conscription in 1935. (2)*

    ☐ Section 4: *Describe **one** decision made by the Allies about the war against Germany at the Teheran Conference, 1943. (2)*

    > Stalin wanted allies to attack Germany in Europe

    ☐ Section 5: *Describe **one** reason why the 'hotline' between the USA and the Soviet Union was set up. (2)*

    ☐ Section 6: *Describe **one** reason why the USA boycotted the Moscow Olympic Games, 1980. (2)*

a   Each question is asking you to write about one of the following:
   o   causation – why something happened
   o   consequence – the effects of an event
   o   change – the changes brought about by an event
   o   a feature.
   Read each of your chosen questions carefully and then decide which of the words above best describes what the question is asking you to write about. Write it in the box.

b   For each of your chosen questions, highlight/underline the key words, including any dates, events or people. Ensure that your answer focuses on these. This is what the question is about.

Activity 2: Understanding the mark scheme

Read the following student answers to the questions from the three sections you are studying.

For each of those three answers:

o   highlight in green a simple statement
o   highlight in blue support for a simple statement
o   decide what level you could give the answer
o   give a brief explanation for your decision about the level.

Hint

This question is worth:

o   one mark for a simple statement (Level 1)

or

o   two marks for a developed statement – this means a supported simple statement (Level 2).

Section 1: *Describe **one** reason why Austria-Hungary seized Bosnia in 1908. (2)*

Student answer	Level	Reason for decision
Austria-Hungary seized Bosnia in 1908 because of fears that Serbia would seize the province first. Austria was frightened of Serbian nationalism.		
Austria-Hungary was frightened of Serbia.		
Austria-Hungary wanted the province.		
Austria-Hungary was determined to prevent a Serbian occupation of Bosnia because of fears of the growth of Serbian nationalism.		

Section 2: *Describe **one** decision which was made about Turkey at the Treaty of Sèvres. (2)*

Student answer	Level	Reason for decision
Turkey lost its empire.		
The Turkish Empire was broken up and much of it was given to France and Britain to govern as mandates on behalf of the League of Nations.		
The treaty took away much of the Turkish land in Europe.		
Turkey lost most of its empire in Europe. Greece gained Eastern Thrace and Smyrna.		

Section 3: *Describe **one** reason why Hitler introduced conscription in 1935. (2)*

Student answer	Level	Reason for decision
Hitler did this to defend Germany.		
Hitler wanted to build up a strong army.		
Germany had a smaller army than many of her neighbouring countries in Europe who were not prepared to disarm to Germany's level.		
Hitler introduced conscription because he needed a large army as he wanted to challenge the Treaty of Versailles and expand eastwards.		

Section 4: *Describe* **one** *decision made by the Allies about the war against Germany at the Teheran Conference, 1943. (2)*

Student answer	Level	Reason for decision
It was agreed that the USSR would begin an offensive in the East.		
The Allies agreed that Britain and the USA would open up a second front in 1944 by a joint invasion of France.		
The Allies would open up a second front.		
At Teheran the Allies agreed that once Germany had been defeated, the USSR would join the war against Japan.		

Section 5: *Describe* **one** *reason why the 'hotline' between the USA and the Soviet Union was set up. (2)*

Student answer	Level	Reason for decision
The 'hotline' was set up because during the Missile Crisis it had taken several hours for the two sides to communicate with each other.		
This was because of slow communications during the Cuban Missile Crisis.		
The 'hotline' was to speed up communications between the USA and the USSR.		
The 'hotline' was set up to speed up communications between the two superpowers and ensure that their leaders could quickly and directly discuss any serious issues.		

Student answer	Level	Reason for decision
The USA was furious with the Soviet invasion of Afghanistan.		
Reagan becomes US president.		
The USA was determined to take a much firmer stance against the Soviet Union as a result of their invasion of Afghanistan in December 1979.		
The USA had decided to take a firm stance against the USSR.		

Answering part (b) questions

Part (b) questions ask you to describe up to three points about an event, policy or decision. It could include causes, events and consequences of the event, policy or decision, e.g. *Describe the key features of the second Moroccan Crisis (1911). (6)* This means you can write about why something happened and its effects.

- In each of your three sections you will be given a choice of two (b) questions. You should only answer one.
- The questions are worth 6 marks. The best answers make two or three developed points.
- This is also marked in two levels as shown in the mark scheme below.

Level	Mark	Descriptor
1	1–3	**Simple statement(s)** These are often very brief and/or generalised e.g. During the Moroccan Crisis, the Germans sent a gunboat to Morocco. • 1 mark for one simple statement • 2 marks for two simple statements • 3 marks for three or more simple statements
2	4–6	**Developed statement** This is a simple statement supported by relevant factual detail. Using the word 'because' often means that the statement has been supported, e.g. During the Moroccan Crisis, the Germans sent a gunboat to Morocco because they were trying to force compensation from France for their takeover of Morocco. • 4–5 marks for one developed statement, according to the degree of support • 5–6 marks for two or more developed statements

Activity 1: Understanding the exam question

1. How long would you expect to spend on (b) questions? Circle your choice.
   - 1 minute
   - 3 minutes
   - 8 minutes

2. Choose the three questions below for the three sections you are studying. For each question:

   a Identify the key events mentioned. You need to ensure that your answer focuses on these. In other words – what is the question about?

   b Identify the key date(s), if this is given in the question.

Section 1: *Describe the events of the second Moroccan Crisis (1911). (6)*

This question is about	
The key date(s)	

Section 2: *Describe the key features of the Assembly and the Council of the League of Nations. (6)*

This question is about	

Section 3: *Describe the key features of the Abyssinian Crisis, 1935–36. (6)*

This question is about	
The key date(s)	

Section 4: *Describe the key features of the Berlin Blockade, 1948–49. (6)*

This question is about	
The key date(s)	

Section 5: *Describe the events of the Soviet invasion of Czechoslovakia, 1968. (6)*

This question is about	
The key date(s)	

Section 6: *Describe the key features of the Intermediate Nuclear Forces (INF) Treaty, 1987. (6)*

This question is about	
The key date(s)	

Read the student answer given below for each of your three sections. Each answer has:

o identified three points
o made developed statements about two of the features.

For each of your three student answers:

o highlight in green each of the key features
o underline any developed statements
o select the developed statement which would most improve the answer. Explain your choice.

Section 1: *Describe the events of the second Moroccan Crisis (1911). (6)*

Student answer

One event of the Moroccan Crisis was the French decision to occupy Morocco in 1911. This was because the ruler of Morocco, the Sultan, asked for French help in crushing a revolt led by rebel tribesmen.

Another event was the German decision to send a gunboat, called the 'Panther', to the Moroccan port of Agadir. This was because the Kaiser was once again testing the Anglo-French Entente and wanted to force compensation from the French for their occupation of Morocco.

A third event was the British decision to support the French.

Possible statements to improve answer

A	There had been a crisis over Morocco in 1905 when the Kaiser had tested the Anglo-French Entente but had been forced to back down at the Algeciras Conference.
B	Another event was when the Kaiser was forced to back down.
C	This was because the British were convinced that the Kaiser was trying to establish a German naval base on the Atlantic at a time of intense Anglo-German naval rivalry.

I chose .... because ....
....

Section 2: *Describe the key features of the Assembly and the Council of the League of Nations. (6)*

Student answer

Every country in the League sent a representative to the Assembly. This was because the Assembly was the parliament of the League which met once a year to make decisions about admitting new members or appointing temporary members.

The Council was a smaller group than the Assembly. This was because it included, at first, only four permanent members, Britain, France, Italy and Japan, and between four and nine temporary members.

A further feature of the Council was its powers.

	Possible statements to improve answer
A	Another key feature was the decisions of the Assembly.
B	It had the powers to impose economic and financial sanctions and could use military force against an aggressor.
C	The League also had a secretariat which was a kind of civil service. It kept records of League meetings and prepared reports for different League agencies.

I chose .... because ....
....

Section 3: *Describe the key features of the Abyssinian Crisis, 1935–36. (6)*

Student answer

The first key feature was the Italian invasion of Abyssinia in October 1935.

A second key feature was the reaction of the League of Nations which imposed sanctions on Italy which included a ban on all imports from Italy. However, these sanctions did not include oil or the closure of the Suez Canal, a vital Italian trade route.

Then there was the Hoare-Laval Pact. This was an agreement between France and Britain which aimed to give Mussolini two-thirds of Abyssinia in return for Mussolini calling off the invasion.

	Possible statements to improve answer
A	One feature was the failure of the League to prevent Japanese aggression in Manchuria in 1931. The League had failed to impose sanctions on Japan.
B	This was because Mussolini wanted to expand the Italian empire in North Africa and wanted revenge for the Italian defeat at Adowa in 1896.
C	Another key feature was Haile Selassie's appeal to the League of Nations.

I chose .... because ....
....

Section 4: *Describe the key features of the Berlin Blockade, 1948–49. (6)*

Student answer

Firstly there was Stalin's decision to introduce the blockade. This was because Stalin wanted to force the Allies, Britain, France and the USA, out of West Berlin which was deep inside the Soviet zone of East Germany.

A second key feature of the blockade was the Berlin Airlift.

A third key feature was Stalin's decision to call off the blockade in May 1949. This was because it had not made the Allies give up West Berlin. On the contrary, Truman was more determined than ever to stand up to the Soviet Union.

Possible statements to improve answer

A	This started in June 1948 and lasted for ten months with the Allies flying over Soviet-controlled East Germany in order to get supplies into West Berlin.
B	Another feature was the Marshall Plan. This was introduced by the USA in 1947 to provide economic aid to all countries in Europe which had been damaged by the Second World War.
C	Another feature was Stalin's reaction to the airlift.

I chose .... because ....

....

Section 5: *Describe the events of the Soviet invasion of Czechoslovakia, 1968. (6)*

Student answer

The first event was the Soviet decision to invade Czechoslovakia.

The second event was the reaction of the Czechs. There was little violent resistance, although many Czechs refused to co-operate with the Soviet troops and demonstrations against the invasion went on until April 1969.

The third event was the arrest of Dubček and other leaders. They were taken to Moscow where they were forced to accept the end of Czechoslovak moves towards democracy. Dubček was not executed but was expelled from the Czech Communist Party.

Possible statements to improve answer

A	Another event was the death of Jan Palach.
B	Another event was the Communist takeover of Czechoslovakia in 1948. They used police and armed militia to seize control and forced out of office the Czechoslovak leader, Edvard Beneš.
C	This was because the Soviets were worried that the reforms introduced by Dubček might spread to other countries in Eastern Europe.

I chose .... because ....

....

Section 6: *Describe the key features of the Intermediate Nuclear Forces (INF) Treaty, 1987. (6)*

Student answer

Firstly there was the decision to sign it which was taken at the third summit conference in Washington between Gorbachev and Reagan, in December 1987, who were both keen to reduce defence spending in their respective countries.

A second feature was the agreement over nuclear and conventional missiles.

A third feature was the stringent verification procedures which were introduced. These were introduced to ensure that the nuclear and conventional weapons were destroyed and the terms of the treaty carried out.

	Possible statements to improve answer
A	The first summit meeting between Reagan and Gorbachev took place at Geneva in November 1985. Though nothing was achieved, the two leaders got on well.
B	The treaty eliminated nuclear and conventional ground-launched ballistic and cruise missiles with a range of 500 to 5500 kilometres.
C	Another key feature was the effect of the INF treaty on relations between the superpowers.

I chose .... because ....
....

Answering part (c) questions

Part (c) is an essay question which asks you to explain causation, e.g. *Explain why rivalry developed between Britain and Germany in the years 1900–14. (12 marks)*

Assess the sample answer below using the mark scheme provided.

- You need to explain at least three causes.
- The best answers make links between these causes and prioritise them.

This is marked in three levels as shown in the mark scheme below.

Level	Mark	Descriptor
1	1–3	**Simple or generalised statements of causation** e.g. One reason for rivalry was the naval race between the two countries. ○ 1 mark for one simple statement ○ 2 marks for two simple statements ○ 3 marks for three simple statements
2	4–9	**Explains why causes led to the given event** e.g. One reason for rivalry was the naval race between the two countries. This was because after the launching of the Dreadnought in 1906, Britain and Germany competed against each other to see who could build the most battleships. Britain was furious that Germany, who already had the most powerful army in the world, was trying to build a navy as big, if not bigger, than that of Britain. This would threaten British control of the sea. ○ 4–5 marks for one developed argument ○ 6–7 marks for two developed arguments ○ 8–9 marks for three or more developed arguments
3	10–12	**Explains how factors are interlinked or prioritises factors** e.g. The growing Anglo-German naval rivalry was worsened by the British support for the French during the two Moroccan Crises of 1905–6 and 1911. However, the most important reason for this rivalry was the naval race. The British strongly resented the potential threat to their control of the sea and their empire by the growth of the German navy. ○ 10–11 marks for linking **or** prioritising factors ○ 11–12 marks for linking **and** prioritising

Activity 1: Understanding the exam question

All part (c) questions are about causation. One important skill in answering this question is selecting what is relevant to the question, rather than just writing everything you know about the event. Remember that you have to write about causes of a particular event: the best answers focus on causation.

Read the three questions for the three sections you are studying. For each question:

- tick the three reasons you would use in your answer
- put a cross next to those which you would not use
- briefly explain why you chose or didn't choose each reason.

Section 1: *Explain why rivalry developed between Britain and Germany in the years 1900–14. (12)*

Reason	Relevant?	Reason for decision
The assassination at Sarajevo in 1914		
The naval race		
Economic rivalry		
The Balkan Wars 1912–13		
Imperial rivalry		

Section 2: *Explain why the League of Nations experienced failures in the 1920s. (12)*

Reason	Relevant?	Reason for decision
Japanese aggression in Manchuria		
Absence of major powers		
Italian invasion of Abyssinia		
Attitude of Britain and France		
Lack of an army		

Section 3: *Explain why international tension increased in Europe in the period from Hitler's takeover of Czechoslovakia (March 1939) to the invasion of Poland (1 September 1939). (12)*

Reason	Relevant?	Reason for decision
The Munich Agreement September 1938		
The German occupation of Prague		
The Anschluss with Austria		
The Nazi-Soviet Pact		
Anglo-French Treaty with Poland		

Section 4: *Explain why there was an uprising in Hungary in 1956. (12)*

Reason	Relevant?	Reason for decision
The effects of the Hungarian uprising		
Khrushchev's secret speech		
The rule of Rakosi		
The impact of Soviet rule		
The Soviet occupation of Hungary in 1944		

Section 5: *Explain why the Soviet and Warsaw Pact countries invaded Czechoslovakia in 1968. (12)*

Reason	Relevant?	Reason for decision
Dubček and the Prague Spring		
The Soviet seizure of Czechoslovakia, 1948		
The consequences of the invasion		
Reactions of Brezhnev		
Influence of East Germany and Poland		

Section 6: *Explain why relations between the USA and the Soviet Union changed in the years 1981–85. (12)*

Reason	Relevant?	Reason for decision
The Soviet invasion of Afghanistan		
Reagan becomes US president		
The Star Wars Programme		
Gorbachev becomes Soviet leader		
The INF Treaty		

Build an answer

The following flow chart shows the steps you should take in preparing an answer to a part (c) question.

Identify the three causes (reasons) that you will explain in your answer. You have done this in the activity on pages 12–13.

Focus on the question. It is about causation, so ensure you write about the reasons why something happened. Do not just tell the story.

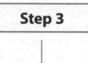

Explain each reason fully. Begin each paragraph with the reason and then explain it fully.

The best answers make links explaining how one reason led to the next. Signpost this by using the word 'link' (e.g.: 'This factor links to the next because…') or by using link words or connectives such as *furthermore, however, in addition, this meant that, as a result of this, moreover.*

Write a conclusion in which you repeat these links and prioritise the reasons. This means you have to decide which of the reasons was the most important and briefly explain why. You could decide all three were equally important, as long as you can explain your judgement.

For the part (c) questions you ticked on pages 12 and 13, complete the following grids to help you plan your answers.

First part (c) question

The question is ....

First reason Give the reason and then fully explain it.	
Link Make a link to the second reason. Remember the link words (see page 14).	
Second reason Give the reason and then fully explain it.	
Link Make a link to the third reason. Remember the link words (see page 14).	
Third reason Give the reason and then fully explain it.	
Prioritising Rank the reasons you selected. Begin with the most important in the inner circle and put the least important in the outer circle.	
Conclusion Explain links between the three reasons and explain which was the most important.	

Second part (c) question

The question is ....

First reason Give the reason and then fully explain it.	
Link Make a link to the second reason. Remember the link words (see page 14).	
Second reason Give the reason and then fully explain it.	
Link Make a link to the third reason. Remember the link words (see page 14).	
Third reason Give the reason and then fully explain it.	
Prioritising Rank the reasons you selected. Begin with the most important in the inner circle and put the least important in the outer circle.	
Conclusion Explain links between the three reasons and explain which was the most important.	

16

Third part (c) question

The question is ....

First reason Give the reason and then fully explain it.	
Link Make a link to the second reason. Remember the link words (see page 14).	
Second reason Give the reason and then fully explain it.	
Link Make a link to the third reason. Remember the link words (see page 14).	
Third reason Give the reason and then fully explain it.	
Prioritising Rank the reasons you selected. Begin with the most important in the inner circle and put the least important in the outer circle.	
Conclusion Explain links between the three reasons and explain which was the most important.	

17

Activity 3: Write an answer

Choose one of the part (c) questions you have planned and write an answer on a separate piece of paper.

- Spend about 15 minutes writing your answer.
- Remember that you need to write about three causes.
- Write a fully developed paragraph on each cause.
- Make links between each cause.
- Prioritise these causes.

Here is the mark scheme to help you with your answer.

Level	Mark	Descriptor
2	4–9	**Explains why causes led to the given event** ○ 4–5 marks for one developed argument ○ 6–7 marks for two developed arguments ○ 8–9 marks for three or more developed arguments
3	10–12	**Explains how factors are interlinked or prioritises factors** ○ 10–11 marks for linking **or** prioritising factors ○ 11–12 marks for linking **and** prioritising factors

Activity 4: Marking your answer

What mark would you give your answer?

Checklist	Mark	Tick
I have fully explained one cause	4–5	
I have fully explained two causes	6–7	
I have fully explained three causes	8–9	
I have shown links between these causes **or** I have prioritised these causes	10–11	
I have linked and prioritised these causes	11–12	

Unit 2: Modern World Depth Study

Introduction

The Unit 2 options

Unit 2 is called a 'Modern World Depth Study'. In it, you study in detail a period of about 20 years. You will be studying one of these three options:

- Option 2A: Germany 1918–39 (see pages 26–44)
- Option 2B: Russia 1917–39 (see pages 45–63)
- Option 2C: The USA 1919–41 (see pages 64–82)

The Unit 2 exam paper

For Unit 2, the exam paper will only have the questions relating to the option that you're studying. You have 75 minutes to answer the questions and there are 57 marks in total for this paper.

The exam paper is split into three main questions: question 1, which has four sub-questions: (a), (b), (c) and (d); question 2 where you have a choice of two sub-questions; and question 3 where you have a choice of two sub-questions.

Each question will test a different skill. Over the next six pages, we'll look at each of these in turn. You'll then need to turn to the pages on your option to practise the different question types.

- Question 1(a) is about making supported inferences and is worth 4 marks (see page 20)
- Question 1(b) is about recalling and describing, and is worth 6 marks (see page 21)
- Question 1(c) is about explaining consequence and is worth 8 marks (see page 22)
- Question 1(d) is about explaining causation and is worth 8 marks (see page 23)
- Question 2 is about explaining how something happened or changed. This is worth 8 marks, plus an additional 3 marks for spelling, punctuation and grammar (see page 24)
- Question 3 is a scaffolding question in which you are given four scaffolding points to help you write your answer. This is worth 16 marks, plus an additional 4 marks for spelling, punctuation and grammar (see page 25).

In questions 2 and 3, there are also marks for your spelling, punctuation and grammar, so you will need to be careful about the quality of your writing. The table below shows how you will be marked across three levels.

Question 2	Question 3	
0 marks	0 marks	Errors severely hinder the meaning of the response or students do not spell, punctuate or use the rules of grammar within the context of the demands of the question.
Level 1: Threshold performance		Students spell, punctuate and use the rules of grammar with reasonable accuracy in the context of the demands of the question. Any errors do not hinder meaning in the response. Where required, they use a limited range of specialist terms appropriately.
1 mark	1 mark	
Level 2: Intermediate performance		Students spell, punctuate and use the rules of grammar with considerable accuracy and general control of meaning in the context of the demands of the question. Where required, they use a good range of specialist terms with facility.
2 marks	2–3 marks	
Level 3: High performance		Students spell, punctuate and use the rules of grammar with consistent accuracy and effective control of meaning in the context of the demands of the question. Where required, they use a wide range of specialist terms adeptly and with precision.
3 marks	4 marks	

How do I answer 1(a) questions?

Question 1(a) is an **inference** question.

For example:

> **2A** *What can you learn from Source A about the Nazi attitude towards the Churches in Germany? (4)*
>
> **2B** *What can you learn from Source A about Stalin's rule of the Soviet Union? (4)*
>
> **2C** *What can you learn from Source A about the position of women in the USA in the 1930s? (4)*

What is meant by an inference?

Making an inference means:
- reading between the lines of what the source says to understand what it is suggesting about a person or event
- squeezing more information from the source than it actually tells you.

Hint
When you are asked an inference question avoid simply repeating information in the source.

How will I be marked?

1(a) questions are worth 4 marks.

You have to make one or more supported inferences. A supported inference means backing up your inference with information, possibly a quote, from the sources.

In other words…

'Last week I played football for the school against our local rivals. We played on a football pitch which was very muddy. We lost 2-1. The referee missed a blatant penalty for us and awarded the other team an offside goal.'

Possible inferences	Possible support for inferences
It had been raining a lot	… because it says that the pitch was very muddy
The pitch had poor drainage	… because it says that the pitch was very muddy
They were unlucky to lose	… because the source says that the referee awarded an offside goal

How do I answer 1(b) questions?

Question 1(b) is a **describe** question.

For example:

2A *Describe the policies of the Nazi government towards the unemployed in the years 1933–39. (6)*

2B *Describe the key features of the Bolshevik Revolution of October 1917. (6)*

2C *Describe the system of mass production used by the Ford Motor Company. (6)*

What is meant by describe?

A 'describe' question tests your ability to select and communicate factual information. This could be about problems, policies or effects. Don't just tell the story. Instead, think about the information and organise it to answer the question.

Hint
The best answers use relevant, precise detail, such as dates or numbers.

How will I be marked?

1(b) questions are worth 6 marks.

You have to make at least two developed statements. A developed statement means that you make a point and then support it with further factual detail. For example, you are asked to describe Nazi policies towards the unemployed in the years 1933–39.

> One Nazi policy was to reduce unemployment through the Labour Service Corps. This was a scheme to provide young men with manual labour jobs. From 1935 it was compulsory for all men aged 18–25 to serve in the corps for six months where they lived in camps, wore uniforms and received very low pay.

The point being made

Detail that supports the point

In other words...

You are asked to describe the problems you have with the homework you get at school.

Unsupported point

> One problem is that sometimes there is too much homework and I cannot finish it.

Support for the point

> For example, every Thursday, I am given an essay for English, which usually takes about two hours to write; history notes to make on a sub-topic which means another one and a half hours; and maths questions to answer, which can take up to 45 minutes. I struggle to finish this in one evening.

How do I answer 1(c) questions?

Question 1(c) is a **consequence** question.

For example:

> **2A** *Explain the effects of Stresemann's economic policies in the years 1924–29. (8)*
>
> **2B** *Explain the effects of Lenin's policy of War Communism on Russia. (8)*
>
> **2C** *Explain the effects of the Wall Street Crash on the USA in the years 1929–32. (8)*

What is meant by consequence?

Consequences are the results or the effects of an event. In other words, what the event led to.

How will I be marked?

1(c) questions are worth 8 marks. You have to give at least two explained statements of consequence **and** show links between these explained statements.

An explained statement means that you give a consequence and then fully explain it with further relevant, precise evidence.

In other words…

You were late for school one day. Your parents ask you, 'What were the effects of you being late for school today?' Here is your answer.

> The first effect of being late for school was that I did not attend my first lesson in history.

The answer focuses on effect. However, it's an unsupported point.

> This meant that I missed an important lesson on Germany in the years 1929–32 in which the teacher explained the causes and impact of the Great Depression on the Weimar Republic and Germany. The class was also given advice on how to write an essay on increased support for the Nazis during this period and time to plan an answer.

Here is an explanation of the consequence given. Notice the precise details given about what was missed and how it affected the student.

> This led to a second consequence, a poor homework essay.

Here is a link to the second consequence.

> I did not understand how to write the homework essay on the reasons why support for the Nazis increased after 1929 and had not had the time to plan an answer. Therefore I wrote a weak essay and ended up with a C/D borderline grade, a much lower grade than usual.

An explanation of a second consequence. Notice also the precise details – the actual homework task and the grade achieved by the student

How do I answer 1(d) questions?

Question 1(d) is a **causation** question.

For example:

> **2A** Explain why the German people disliked the Treaty of Versailles. (8)
>
> **2B** Explain why Stalin became leader of the Soviet Union. (8)
>
> **2C** Explain why organised crime grew in the USA in the 1920s. (8)

What is meant by causation?

Causation means explaining the reasons why an event happened.

How will I be marked?

1(d) questions are worth 8 marks. You have to give two explained statements on causation and show links between these explained statements **or** explain which you think was the more important reason.

Remember

An explained statement means that you give a cause and then fully explain it with further relevant, precise evidence.

In other words…

Your parents receive your school report and say to you, 'Explain why you did not do well in your history exam.' Here is your answer.

> One reason I did not do well was because I did not revise thoroughly for the exam.

The answer focuses on causation. However, it's an unsupported point.

> This was because I did not plan my revision and left it far too late to start, which meant that I had to rush my revision and did not have a thorough enough knowledge of three periods of international relations and my depth study plus the key features of each of the revision topics.

Here an explanation has been given. Notice the precise details given about what was missed.

> As a result of this lack of knowledge and understanding, my exam answers were not very good. This was the second reason why I did not do well. I did not have enough precise details about key events and was not able to write enough, especially for the higher mark exam questions, to be able to reach the higher level marks. I also got confused with dates and the order of events which also brought down my final marks.

Links first to second reason.

An explanation for the second reason is given.

> Overall, the main reason why I did so badly was that I did not work out a revision plan, which meant that I did not start my revision until far too close to the examinations and therefore had too little knowledge to do well in the exam.

Reasons are prioritised.

How do I answer questions 2(a) and 2(b)

In question 2, you are given a choice of two questions but you should only answer one.

Question 2(a) is about **process** or **change** – the way in which something developed or changed. For example:

2A *Explain how Hitler was able to overcome opposition to his government in the years 1933–34. (8)*	**2B** *Explain how the Bolsheviks overcame opposition to their rule in the years 1917–24. (8)*	**2C** *Explain how Roosevelt dealt with the problems of the banks in 1933. (8)*

A **process** question is asking you to explain how something happened, such as how you prepared for your mock exams. You could explain how you organised a revision timetable and revised different subjects.

A **change** question is asking you to write about change over a period of time. Use change words such as 'more', 'less', 'better', 'increased', 'worsened', 'stayed the same'.

In other words…

Here is an example of an everyday change. The words in red are words which show change.

I was not very good at history last year in Year 9 and achieved less than half marks because I had very little interest in the subject. However things have improved in Year 10, and I achieved over 75% in my end of term exam. I am better at the subject because we are studying much more interesting topics such as Hitler's rise to power. My homework has improved because I have put in much more effort and preparation and I have achieved better marks than the year before.

Question 2(b) is also about **process** or **change**. For example:

2A *Explain how the position of Jews in Germany changed in the years 1933–39. (8)*	**2B** *Explain how the Provisional Government lost support during 1917. (8)*	**2C** *Explain how the lives of farmers changed in the years 1919–29. (8)*

How will I be marked?

Both 2(a) and 2(b) are worth 8 marks. You have to:
- give two explained statements of ways in which change happened or of changes
- show links between these explained statements or prioritise the changes.

An explained statement means that you write a point about a **process** or **change** and then fully explain it with precise evidence. In question 2, there are also 3 marks available for spelling, punctuation and grammar. Take extra care over your writing and try to leave time to check your answer at the end.

How do I answer questions 3(a) and 3(b)?

In question 3, you are given a choice of two questions but you should only answer one.

Question 3 is a **scaffolding** question because you are given a scaffold or framework (the four bullet points) to help you answer the question. For example:

2A *Was the growth of unemployment after 1929 the most important reason why the Nazi Party was able to take power in Germany in 1933? Explain your answer. (16)*

- The growth of unemployment after 1929
- Fear of communism
- Nazi use of propaganda
- The role of the SA

2B *Was the opposition of peasants and town workers the main reason why the Tsar was forced to abdicate in 1917? Explain your answer. (16)*

- Opposition of peasants and town workers
- Russia's poor performance in the First World War
- The weaknesses of Tsar Nicholas II
- The events in Petrograd in January and February 1917

2C *Was motor car ownership the most important reason for improvements in the way of life for many Americans in the 1920s? Explain your answer. (16)*

- Motor car ownership
- New consumer goods
- New forms of entertainment
- High levels of prosperity

How will I be marked?

This is the highest scoring question you will have to answer as it is worth 16 marks, plus 4 marks for spelling, punctuation and grammar. You have to:
- explain the importance of at least three factors
- make a judgement on the relative importance of all of the factors.

In other words…

Was revision planning the most important reason you did well in your mock exams? Explain your answer.

You may use the following in your answer and any other information of your own.
- Revision planning
- Thorough revision of the topics for each exam
- Exam technique
- Choice of questions

If you were answering the question you would be expected to:
- explain about your revision planning and make a judgement on its importance
- explain the importance of the other three reasons in the scaffolding or other points of your own
- make a final judgement showing the inter-relationship and interdependence of all four reasons.

Option 2A: Germany 1918–39

Question 1(a)

Question 1(a) is an inference question (see page 20).

Activity 1: Understanding the exam question

Source A is about women in Nazi Germany. Read Source A and the exam question below.

Source A: From a book on the history of Germany, published in 1985.

> Women in Germany were forced to stay at home. Within months of the Nazis coming to power, many women doctors and civil servants were sacked from their jobs. Then women lawyers and teachers were dismissed. By 1939 there were few women left in professional jobs. The Nazi Party tried to stop women following fashions. Make-up and wearing trousers were frowned upon. Hair was to be arranged either in buns or in plaits. Slimming was discouraged because being slim was not thought to be good for having children.

What can you learn from Source A about the treatment of women in Nazi Germany? (4)

This question is worth 4 marks.

1. How long would you expect an answer to be? Ring your choice.
    o   Two sentences
    o   One paragraph
    o   Two paragraphs

2. Approximately how long should you spend answering this question? Ring your choice.
    o   2 minutes
    o   6 minutes
    o   10 minutes

3. What is the question asking you to do? Ring your choice.
    o   Make inferences from the source
    o   Make supported inferences from the source
    o   Summarise the source

Activity 2: Mark an answer

What mark would you give the following student answers to the question in Activity 1? Use the mark scheme to help you decide.

Level	Mark	Descriptor
1	1	Students do no more than copy/paraphrase the source.
2	2–3	**Makes unsupported inferences** Inference given but not supported by source o 2 marks for one unsupported inference o 3 marks for two unsupported inferences
3	4	**Makes supported inferences** Inference given and it is supported by the source, e.g. 'because the source tells me…' One well-supported inference can be sufficient.

	Student answers	Mark
A	Women were treated as second-class citizens in Nazi Germany.	
B	By 1939 there were few women in professional jobs.	
C	Women were encouraged not to follow careers in Nazi Germany and were being prepared for motherhood in Nazi Germany.	
D	Women were treated as second-class citizens in Nazi Germany because the source tells us they were sacked from professional jobs such as lawyers and teachers.	
E	Women were given no real choice about their appearance in Nazi Germany. This is shown in the source when it says it was frowned upon to wear make-up and trousers. Their hair had to be arranged in a bun or in plaits.	

Activity 3: Improving an answer

Here is an answer which is an unsupported inference.

Women were much controlled by the state in Nazi Germany.

Improve this answer by writing below how this inference is supported by the source.

Activity 4: Making a supported inference

Source B: From a history of the modern world, published in 2000.

By 1934, the SA had outlived its usefulness. It had been used to guard large Nazi Party meetings and demonstrations and to intimidate opponents, such as communists. The SA had approximately two million members, many of them unemployed. Their continued violence was giving a bad reputation to the Nazi regime. On the night of 29 June 1934, Hitler used the SS to arrest and shoot leading members of the SA, including Ernst Röhm. Over the next few days, up to 200 people, including politicians, were killed. These events became known as the 'Night of the Long Knives'.

What can you learn from Source B about the power of the Nazis in Germany? (4)

Complete the sentences below to give a Level 3 answer to this question.

This source suggests that ....

....

I know that because the source says ....

....

Question 1(b)

Question 1(b) is a describe question (see page 21).

Activity 1: Understanding the exam question

Describe the policies of the Nazi government towards the young in the years 1933–39. (6)

1. Look at the marks for this question. How much would you expect to write in your answer? Ring your choice.
   - Two sentences
   - Two/three paragraphs
   - Three/four paragraphs

2. How long do you think you should spend answering this question? Ring your choice.
   - 10 minutes
   - 15 minutes
   - 20 minutes

3. a Underline the word in the question which is telling you what to do, the 'command' word.

   b Highlight key words such as dates, events or people.

4. Now decide what the question is asking you to do. Ring your choice.
   - Explain causation
   - Describe what happened
   - Explain consequence

Activity 2: Mark an answer

Read the answer below to the question in Activity 1.
- **First** highlight in blue any simple statements.
- **Next** highlight in green any supporting details.
- **Then** using the mark scheme below, decide what mark to give the answer.
  Tick the box in the Checklist.
- **Finally** give a brief explanation for your choice.

Student answer

One of Hitler's policies towards the young was to set up the Hitler Youth organisation. He made sure that all boys joined it. The Hitler Youth organisations seemed like good fun to German children, but really they were a means of spreading Nazi propaganda and encouraging the boys to focus on the military. There was an emphasis on fitness with outdoor activities and long walks.

Another policy was education which was taken over by the state and used to put across the Nazi message.

Level	Mark	Descriptor
2	4–6	**Developed statement(s)** Simple statement(s) with additional supporting material. • 4–5 marks for one developed statement • 5–6 marks for two or more developed statements

Hint

Using the words 'for example' often means that the statement has been supported.

Checklist	Mark	Tick
One developed statement	4	
One well-developed statement	5	
Two developed statements	6	

Explanation ....

....

Activity 3: Improve an answer

Which of the following statements would improve the answer in Activity 2? Explain your choice.

	Possible additional statements	Tick
A	The Nazis also controlled the lives of women in Nazi Germany. They were discouraged from having careers with many losing their professional jobs, especially teachers and doctors. Instead they were encouraged to marry and have children.	
B	Boys spent more time in PE and subjects such as Race Studies were introduced. Girls were taught skills that would be useful in the home, because their role was to be mothers and homemakers, so sewing and cooking were important.	
C	The Nazis also controlled the lives of girls in Nazi Germany through the League of German Girls, which was the female version of the Hitler Youth.	
I chose .... because		

Activity 4: Plan and write an answer

1. Plan an answer to the following question, using the framework below.

Describe the economic policies of Gustav Stresemann in the years 1924–29. (6)

The first policy was	
Describe it	
The second policy was	
Describe it	

2. Now write a full answer to this question on a separate piece of paper.

Question 1(c)

Question 1(c) is a consequence question (see page 22).

Activity 1: Understanding the exam question

Explain the effects of Stresemann's economic policies in the years 1924–29. (8)

1. How long do you think you should spend answering an 8-mark question? Ring your choice.
    - 6 minutes
    - 12 minutes
    - 18 minutes

2. How much do you think you're expected to write in that time? Ring your choice.
    - Two sentences
    - Two/three paragraphs
    - Three/four paragraphs

Activity 2: Understanding the exam question

Identify which of the following are aims and which are effects of Stresemann's policies. Tick the correct column.

		Aim	Effect
A	Stresemann introduced the Rentenmark in order to stabilise the German currency.		
B	One consequence of the new currency was that the currency was stabilised.		
C	One consequence of the Dawes plan was that Germany was now able to make reparations payments that it could afford.		
D	The Dawes Plan was introduced to try to solve the problem of German reparations payments.		
E	Loans from the USA provided investment which enabled Germany to invest in its industries.		
F	Stresemann encouraged loans from the USA as a way of helping to revive the German economy.		

How do I build an answer?

Step 1
Choose two of the effects you have identified in Activity 2.

Step 2
Explain each effect fully. Begin each paragraph with the effect and then fully explain it. Aim to write one extended paragraph on each effect.

Step 3

The best answers make links. This means explaining how one effect led to or is linked to the next. Signpost by using the word 'link'. Link words or connectives would also help, such as *furthermore, in addition, this meant that, as a result of this, moreover*.

Step 4

Write a conclusion in which you summarise your two effects and reinforce the links between them.

Activity 3: Plan your answer

Explain the effects of the Wall Street Crash on the USA in the years 1929–32. (8)

Complete the following grid to plan your answer to this question using the advice in the **How do I build an answer?** section above.

First effect	Give the effect
Explanation	Explain it
Link	Make a link to the second effect. Remember the link words: *furthermore, in addition, this meant that, as a result of this, moreover.*
Second effect	Give the effect
Explanation	Explain it
Conclusion	Summarise the two effects and reinforce the links between them

Activity 4: Planning an answer

The following extracts make up an answer to the question below. Put them into the correct order, using the planning grid below.

Explain the effects of the Enabling Act (1933) in Germany. (8)

Extract A

He could now pass laws without the permission of the Reichstag and used these powers to create a dictatorship of the Nazi Party. For example, by June 1933 he had banned the larger opposition parties, arrested their leaders and ordered the SA to destroy their headquarters. Germany became a one-party state with the Nazis the only legal party.

Extract B

Overall, the Enabling Act gave Hitler the powers to create a dictatorship by removing any potential opposition including other political parties as well as the German trade unions.

Extract C

One consequence of the Enabling Act was that Hitler was now a dictator.

Extract D

Hitler believed trade unions could threaten his dictatorship by organising strikes. In May 1933, Hitler used the powers of the Enabling Act to ban all trade unions. All workers and employers were now to be members of the Labour Front, which enabled the Nazis to control German workers.

Extract E

As well as removing political opposition, he also used the Enabling Act to get rid of any other potential threats.

Extract F

Therefore, a second consequence of the Enabling Law was the removal of trade unions in Germany.

Planning grid

	Extract (A, B, C, D, E or F)
First explained effect	
Link to second effect	
Second explained effect	
Conclusion	

Activity 5: Plan and write an answer

On a separate piece of paper, plan and write an answer to the following question.

Explain the effects of Nazi policies on the Jews in the years 1933–39. (8)

Remember

You need to:
o fully explain two effects
o show links between the two effects.

Question 1(d)

Question 1(d) is a causation question (see page 23).

Activity 1: Understanding the exam question

Explain why the German people disliked the Treaty of Versailles. (8)

1. Look at the marks for this question. How much would you expect to write in your answer? Ring your choice.
   - Two sentences
   - Two/three paragraphs
   - Three/four paragraphs

2. How long do you think you should spend answering this question? Ring your choice.
   - 6 minutes
   - 12 minutes
   - 18 minutes

3. a Underline the 'command' word.

   b Highlight key words such as dates, events or people.

4. Decide what the question is asking you to do. Ring your choice.
   - Explain causation
   - Describe what happened
   - Explain consequence

Activity 2: Understanding the exam question

One important skill in answering 1(d) questions is selecting what is relevant to the question. The best answers focus on causation rather than simply listing everything about the event.

Look at the factors in the table below and:
- tick the two reasons you would use in your answer to the question in Activity 1
- put a cross next to those which you would not use in an answer to the question
- briefly explain why you have decided each reason is relevant or not relevant.

Factor	Relevant? ✓ or X	Explanation
The new Weimar Constitution		
Territorial terms of the Treaty		
Military terms of the Treaty		
The Spartacist Uprising		
The Kapp Putsch		

Activity 3: Using the mark scheme

Read the following answer to the question in Activity 1.

Student answer

The Germans were annoyed about the territorial terms of the Treaty. In the Treaty the Germans lost much land including Alsace-Lorraine to France and the Polish Corridor. The Germans had captured Alsace-Lorraine from the French in 1871 and possessing this disputed territory was a matter of national honour. Furthermore, the loss of the Polish Corridor divided East Prussia from the rest of Germany. In addition all Germany's colonies were handed over to the victorious Allies.

The Germans also hated the military terms of the Treaty of Versailles.

What mark would you give this answer? Tick the box in the Checklist table below. Give a brief explanation for your choice.

Checklist	Mark(s)	Tick
Two developed statements	5	
One explained cause	6–7	
Two explained causes	7–8	
Links or prioritises the causes	8	

Explanation ....

....

Activity 4: Improve an answer

This answer could be improved by linking the two causes or by prioritising the causes.

1. Which of the following statements would **link** the two causes? Explain your choice(s).

A	Another reason that Germany disliked the Treaty was because of the territorial terms.
B	Although upset with the territorial losses, many Germans disliked even more the military restrictions imposed by the Treaty of Versailles.
C	Germans were appalled by the terms they had to accept, both in the military restrictions and in the loss of territory.

I would choose ...... because ....

2. Which of the following statements **prioritise** the causes? Explain your choice(s).

A	The most important reason was the military restrictions because Germany had a long tradition of strong armed forces and had the strongest army before the war.
B	The military restrictions and the territorial losses were both important.
C	The territorial losses were more important than the military gains.

I would choose ...... because ....

3. Which of the following extracts would either **improve or not improve** the answer? Explain each decision.

	Student answers	Improve? ✓/✗	Explanation
A	The Germans hated the war guilt clause. This was because they did not believe that they were to blame for the First World War.		
B	The terms of the Treaty of Versailles were publicised in May 1919. These included military restrictions, loss of territory and colonies, the war guilt clause and the payment of reparations. The amount of reparations to be paid was not fixed until 1920. Some Germans argued that the army had been 'stabbed in the back' by the politicians.		
C	An army of 100,000 seemed too small to defend Germany against its neighbours. Moreover, they were also a proud nation so having to agree to restrictions on which parts of their country they could station their troops, especially the demilitarisation of the Rhineland, was a real blow to their pride and made them dislike the Treaty.		

Activity 5: Plan and write an answer

Explain why Germany was difficult to govern in the years 1919–22. (8)

1. Plan an answer to this question in the grid below.

First explained reason	
Link to second reason	
Second explained reason	
Conclusion – prioritise the reasons	

2. Now write a full answer on a separate piece of paper.

Question 2(a)

Question 2(a) is about process – the way in which something happened – or about change (see page 24).

Activity 1: Understanding the exam question

Explain how Hitler was able to overcome opposition to his government in the years 1933–34. (8)

1. How long do you think you should spend answering an 8-mark question? Ring your choice.
   - 6 minutes
   - 12 minutes
   - 18 minutes

2. How much do you think you're expected to write in that time? Ring your choice.
   - Two sentences
   - One paragraph
   - Two/three paragraphs

3. a Underline the command word.
   b Highlight key words, such as dates, events or people.

4. Decide what the question is asking you to do. Ring your choice.
   - Explain causation
   - Explain how something happened
   - Explain consequence

> **Remember**
>
> In question 2 there are 3 additional marks available for spelling, punctuation and grammar. Pay careful attention to these (see page 44).

Activity 2: Understanding the exam question

Look at the four different events below.

Highlight in green those which are relevant to this question.

The Reichstag Fire in February 1933 which Hitler used as an excuse to get rid of the communists
The Nuremberg Laws of 1935 which denied Jews German citizenship
The Munich Putsch of 1923 when Hitler tried to seize power
The Night of the Long Knives in June 1934 when Hitler removed the SA

How do I build an answer?

Step 1
Select two of the events you have identified in Activity 2.

Step 2
Begin each paragraph with the way each event developed and then fully explain it. Aim to write two or three sentences on each way.

> **Hint**
>
> Focus on the question. It is about the ways in which things developed, so ensure you write about these ways. Do not just tell the story.

Step 3

The best answers make links. This means explaining how one way led to or is linked to the next. Signpost this by using the word 'link'. Link words or connectives would also help, such as *furthermore, in addition, this meant that, as a result of this, moreover*.

Step 4

Write a conclusion. Summarise your two ways and reinforce the links between them.

Activity 4: Planning the answer

Explain how Hitler was able to overcome opposition to his government in the years 1933–34. (8)

Complete the following grid to plan your answer to this question using the advice in the **How do I build an answer**? section above.

First way	Give the way
Explanation	Explain it
Link	Make a link to the second way. Remember the link words: *furthermore, however, in addition, this meant that, as a result of this, moreover.*
Second way	Give the way
Explanation	Explain it
Conclusion	Summarise the two ways and reinforce the links between them

Question 2(b)

Question 2(b) is also about process or change (see page 24).

(see page 24)

Activity 1: Understanding the exam question

Explain how the position of Jews in Germany changed in the years 1933–39. (8)

Tick the following student answers to this question which focus on the idea of **change**.

	Student answers	Tick
A	Hitler persecuted the Jews in the years 1933–39 because he wanted to create a pure Aryan race.	
B	The position of Jews remained much the same in 1936 as the Nazis relaxed their campaign due to the potential bad publicity of the Berlin Olympics.	
C	In 1933 there was a boycott of Jews' shops. In the same year Jews were banned from posts in the civil service. In 1935 the Nazis introduced the Nuremberg Laws.	
D	The position of the Jews grew much worse after the events of Kristallnacht in 1938, with many rounded up and sent to concentration camps.	
E	One of the worst changes in the position of the Jews was the Nuremberg Laws of 1935 which took away many of their basic rights.	

Activity 2: Using the mark scheme

Level	Mark	Descriptor
3	6–8	**Developed explanation of change** One or more changes are explained, supported by selected knowledge ○ 6–7 marks for one explained change ○ 7–8 marks for two or more explained changes ○ 8 marks for answers which prioritise changes **or** show links between them

What mark would you give this answer? Use the mark scheme above. Explain your choice.

Student answer

The Nuremberg Laws of 1935 worsened the position of Jews. They had now become second-rate citizens in their own country. They were singled out for special treatment, were deprived of citizenship and not allowed to vote. In addition Jews were forbidden to marry or have a relationship with non-Jewish people in Germany. This was a significant change from the position before 1933.

I would give this .... marks because ....
....

Activity 3: Improve an answer

1. Which of the following extracts would **improve/not improve** the answer? Explain each decision.

Student answers		Improve? ✔ or ✘	Explanation
A	In 1933 the SA organised a boycott of Jewish shops and businesses. They painted 'Jude' or Jew on windows and tried to persuade people not to enter. A new law excluded Jews from government jobs and Jews were banned from inheriting land. In 1934 local councils banned Jews from public places.		
B	Jewish school children were often treated badly in schools and victimised by teachers and other students.		
C	Kristallnacht was another change for the worse, especially as Hitler officially blamed the Jews themselves for having provoked the attacks. It was followed by even worse treatment of the Jews with 30,000 rounded up and sent to concentration camps and, in the following year, Jews evicted from their homes and forced into ghettos.		

2. Which of the following would now **link** the two changes in the answer? Explain your choice(s).

A	Another reason that the position of the Jews in Germany changed was because of Kristallnacht.
B	For the most part things got worse for the Jews in Germany as was shown by the Nuremberg Laws of 1935 and Kristallnacht three years later.
C	The position of the Jews changed even more in 1938 during and after the events of Kristallnacht.

I would choose ...... because ....
....

Activity 4: Plan and write an answer

Explain how the position of women in Germany changed in the years 1933–39. (8)

1. Plan an answer to this question in the grid below.

First explained change	
Link to second change	
Second explained change	
Conclusion – link the changes	

2. Now write a full answer to this question on a separate piece of paper.

Question 3

Question 3 is a scaffolding question (see page 25).

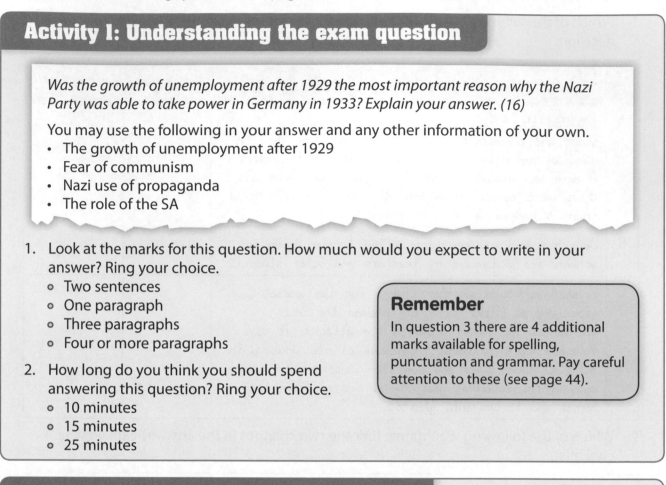

Activity 1: Understanding the exam question

Was the growth of unemployment after 1929 the most important reason why the Nazi Party was able to take power in Germany in 1933? Explain your answer. (16)

You may use the following in your answer and any other information of your own.
- The growth of unemployment after 1929
- Fear of communism
- Nazi use of propaganda
- The role of the SA

1. Look at the marks for this question. How much would you expect to write in your answer? Ring your choice.
   - Two sentences
   - One paragraph
   - Three paragraphs
   - Four or more paragraphs

2. How long do you think you should spend answering this question? Ring your choice.
   - 10 minutes
   - 15 minutes
   - 25 minutes

Remember
In question 3 there are 4 additional marks available for spelling, punctuation and grammar. Pay careful attention to these (see page 44).

Activity 2: What is the question about?

1. Which of the following should you include in your answer? Underline your choice(s).
   - Brief points on the scaffolding factors
   - Developed statements on two or more of the factors
   - Explanation of at least two of the factors
   - Judgements on the importance of at least three of the factors

2. What is the focus of the question? Ring your choice.
   - Hitler's rise to power, 1929–33
   - The early Nazi Party, 1919–23
   - The removal of opposition, 1933–34

Remember
Ensure you focus on the actual question. What is it asking you to do? It is not asking you to write as much as you know about the factors but to emphasise supported judgements on these factors (or others of your own) showing how they interacted.

How do I build an answer?

Step 1 First scaffolding point
Begin by writing a paragraph on the factor mentioned in the question, which will also be the first scaffolding point. Explain its importance and support this with your own knowledge.

Step 2 Further scaffolding points
Next, write a paragraph on each of the other scaffolding points. Explain the importance of each and support this with your own knowledge.

Step 3 Conclusion
You could begin with the word 'overall'. In your conclusion, explain how each of the factors is important by showing the links or relationship between them.

Activity 3: Writing your conclusion

1. Write notes about the four factors in the boxes.

2. For your conclusion you have to explain why most, if not all, of the four factors were important and how they combined. In other words, the interrelationship or links between the factors in bringing about the event, or how the factors were dependent on each other. On the mind map:

    o   draw lines to show links between the factors

    o   on these lines, briefly explain how the two factors were linked or dependent on each other. One example has been done for you.

Unemployment after 1929

Importance

Explanation

Nazi use of propaganda

Importance

Explanation

Unemployed began to support the communist party

Why the Nazi Party was able to take power in Germany in 1933

Fear of communists

Importance

Explanation

Role of the SA

Importance

Explanation

Activity 4: Using the mark scheme

Level	Mark	Descriptor
3	9–12	**Developed explanation of causation** ○ 9–10 marks for two or more explained factors ○ 11–12 marks for two or more explained factors with a judgement on why one is more important than one other.
4	13–16	**A sustained argument** This means the answer focuses throughout on the relative importance of the factors. ○ 13–14 marks for judgements on the relative importance of more than two of the factors ○ 15–16 marks for showing the relative importance of all of the factors and illustrating that 'one most important reason' on its own could not provide a satisfactory explanation.

1. What level would you give the following answer? Give reasons for your decision.

Student answer

The growth in unemployment was important because it meant that the Nazis could make promises to provide more jobs and this increased support for Hitler and the Party. In 1929 there was the Wall Street Crash in America which started a world depression. Many German businesses collapsed and this led to higher unemployment. This had reached six million by 1932. Many of the unemployed were desperate and began to support the Nazis and the Communists.

Propaganda was also important in increasing support for the Nazis. The constant messages on posters, in public meetings and on the radio persuaded many people that the Nazis were the saviours of Germany. Goebbels was in charge of propaganda and used all different methods to get people to support the Nazi Party. These included the use of posters, newspapers and the radio. He even organised it so that Hitler could be flown from place to place to make speeches.

The SA were also important in increasing support for the Nazis. This was Hitler's private army and by 1932 there were 300,000 members of the SA. They were used to protect the Nazi meetings and to attack the meetings of their opponents, especially the Communists. Germans were particularly impressed with the discipline of the SA especially when they marched round city centres.

Overall, the most important reason for increased support for the Nazis was propaganda because this got the Nazi message across to many Germans.

Level:	**Reason:**

2. Suggest two improvements to this answer.

First improvement	
Second improvement	

Activity 5: Plan and write an answer

Was the Spartacist uprising the most important problem faced by the Weimar Republic in the years 1919–24? Explain your answer. (16)

You may use the following in your answer and any other information of your own.
- The Spartacist uprising
- Weaknesses in the Constitution
- The Munich Putsch
- The French occupation of the Ruhr

1. Plan an answer to the question by writing notes in the grid.

The first problem	Explain the problem of the Spartacists Make a judgement on their importance
The second problem	Explain the problem caused by a second scaffolding point Make a judgement on its importance
The third problem	Explain the problem caused by a third scaffolding point Make a judgement on its importance
The fourth problem	Explain the problem caused by a fourth scaffolding point Make a judgement on its importance
Conclusion	Make a judgement on the relative importance of all four problems, showing how they combined

2. Now write your full answer on a separate piece of paper. Make sure you are careful to spell and punctuate correctly and use grammar well, and check your answer over once you've finished.

Spelling, punctuation and grammar

In both question 2 and question 3 of Unit 2, the additional marks for spelling, punctuation and grammar are awarded across three levels. The mark scheme on page 19 shows how your answers will be assessed.

Now let's look at some examples. Read the extracts below from three student answers to the question on page 38 and:

o circle any spelling mistakes

o underline any errors of punctuation or grammar

o decide what level you think each answer should be in and write it next to the answer.

	Student answer	Level
A	The first change in the position of Jews was in 1933 when the SA organised a boycott of Jewish shops and businesses. They painted 'Jude' (Jew) on windows and tried to persuade people not to enter. The situation got even worse when a new law excluded Jews from government jobs and Jews were banned from inheriting land.	
B	The Nuremburg Laws of 1935 made the position of Jews worse, they had now become second rate citizens in there own country. They were singled out for special treatment and deprived of citizenship and not allowed to vote, this was a significant change from the position before 1933.	
C	The position of the jews changed very little in 1936 because Nazis stopped persercuting them so much because they was holding the olimpic games in berlin and wanted to put on a good show for the rest of the world and not appear to be treating the jews badly	

Option 2B: Russia 1917–39

Question 1(a)

Question 1(a) is an inference question (see page 20).

Activity 1: Understanding the exam question

Source A is about Stalin's rule. Read the source and then answer the questions that follow.

Source A: From a history of the modern world, published in 2000.

> Stalin's achievements were constantly praised. Part of Stalin's approach was to use the 'cult of personality'. The Soviet people were taught that Stalin was an all-powerful and all-knowing leader. He was the father figure who ruled with all their interests at heart. His image was everywhere – in posters, statues and books. There was even a set of eight recordings made of his speeches.

What can you learn from Source A about Stalin's rule of the Soviet Union? (4)

This question is worth 4 marks.

1. How long would you expect your answer to be? Ring your choice.
    - Two sentences
    - One paragraph
    - Two paragraphs

2. Approximately how long should you spend answering this question? Ring your choice.
    - 2 minutes
    - 6 minutes
    - 10 minutes

3. What is the question asking you to do? Ring your choice.
    - Make inferences from the source
    - Make supported inferences from the source
    - Summarise the source

Activity 2: Mark an answer

What mark would you give the following student answers to the question in Activity 1? Use the mark scheme below to help you decide.

Level	Mark	Descriptor
1	1	Students do no more than copy/paraphrase the source.
2	2–3	**Makes unsupported inferences** Inference given but not supported by source • 2 marks for one unsupported inference • 3 marks for two unsupported inferences
3	4	**Makes supported inferences** Inference given and it is supported by the source, e.g. 'because the source tells me…' One well-supported inference is sufficient.

	Student answers	Mark
A	I can learn that Stalin's rule was one where his own personal characteristics were considered very important.	
B	We can learn that Stalin was the father figure and there was even a set of eight recordings made of his speeches.	
C	We can learn that propaganda was used very effectively to create the cult of personality.	
D	I can learn that Stalin's rule was one where his own personal characteristics were considered very important. The source says that the cult of personality was used to show him as a father figure with the people's interests at heart.	
E	We can learn that Stalin's achievements were constantly praised. Part of Stalin's approach was to use the cult of personality.	

Activity 3: Improving an answer

Here is an answer which is an unsupported inference.

We can learn that the Soviet people would have been greatly influenced by the cult of personality.

Improve the answer by adding support for the inference from the source.

Activity 4: Making a supported inference

Source A: From a history of Russia, published in 2009.

Stalin's propaganda stressed the equality of the republics of the Soviet Union. Posters and photos often showed him with people from these regions in their national dress. Until the early 1930s, the state gave support to local languages. But during enforced collectivisation, the greatest opposition came from the regions, which were heavily purged. From 1932, Stalin saw support for the regional identity of the ethnic minorities as anti-communist.

What can you learn from Source A about Stalin's attitude towards the ethnic minorities in the Soviet Union? (4)

Complete the sentences below to give a Level 3 answer to this question.

This source suggests that..

....

I know that because the source says..

....

Question 1(b)

Question 1(b) is a describe question (see page 21).

Activity 1: Understanding the exam question

Describe the key features of the Bolshevik Revolution of October 1917. (6)

1. Look at the marks for this question. How much would you expect to write in your answer? Ring your choice.
   - Two sentences
   - Two/three paragraphs
   - Three/four paragraphs

2. How long do you think you should spend answering this question? Ring your choice.
   - 10 minutes
   - 15 minutes
   - 20 minutes

3. a Underline the word in the question which is telling you what to do, the 'command' word.
   b Highlight key words such as dates, events or people.

4. Now decide what the question is asking you to do. Ring your choice.
   - Explain causation
   - Describe what happened
   - Explain consequence

Activity 2: Mark an answer

Read the answer below to the question in Activity 1.
- **First** highlight in blue any simple statements.
- **Next** highlight in green any supporting detail.
- **Then** using the mark scheme below, decide what mark to give the answer. Tick the box in the Checklist.
- **Finally** give a brief explanation for your choice.

Student answer
One key feature was the planning that went into the takeover. Trotsky was made Chairman of the Military Committee and organised the revolution. On 21 October most army units in Petrograd promised to support Trotsky and the Military Revolutionary Committee. Two days later, the soldiers in the main fort of the city agreed to obey the Military Revolutionary Committee. A second key feature was the actual takeover of Petrograd.

Checklist	Mark	Tick
One developed statement	4	
One well-developed statement	5	
Two developed statements	6	

Explanation ....

....

Activity 3: Improve an answer

Which of the following statements would improve the answer in Activity 2? Explain your choice.

	Possible additional statements	Tick
A	By the end of 1917, nearly all Russia was in soviet hands. This did not mean that Lenin and the Bolsheviks had total control of Russia. Not all the soviets were run by Bolsheviks and, in the countryside, most peasants supported the Socialist Revolutionaries.	
B	On the night of the 24 October, Trotsky's plans were put into action. Key buildings in Petrograd, such as telegraph offices and railway stations, were captured by the Bolsheviks, and road blocks were set up on the city's bridges and surrounding the Winter Palace where the Provisional Government was in session.	
C	Lenin returned to Russia in April 1917. He was put in a sealed train and sent across Germany and Sweden before arriving in Petrograd. Lenin made it clear to his followers that he would not support the Provisional Government and set out his plans for a revolution in the April Theses.	
I chose .... because		

Activity 4: Plan and write an answer

1. Plan an answer to the following question, using the framework below.

Describe the key features of the Kornilov Revolt. (6)

State what the first feature was	
Describe it	
State a second feature	
Describe it	

2. Now write a full answer to this question on a separate piece of paper.

Question 1(c)

Question 1(c) is a consequence question (see page 22).

Activity 1: Understanding the exam question

Explain the effects of Lenin's policy of War Communism on Russia. (8)

1. How long do you think you should spend answering an 8-mark question? Ring your choice.
   - 6 minutes
   - 12 minutes
   - 18 minutes

2. How much do you think you're expected to write in that time? Ring your choice.
   - Two sentences
   - Two/three paragraphs
   - Three/four paragraphs

Activity 2: Understanding the exam question

Identify which of the following are aims and which are effects of Lenin's policy of War Communism. Tick the relevant column.

		Aim	Effect
A	War Communism supplied the Red Army with food and enabled the victory over the Whites during the Civil War		
B	Lenin introduced War Communism in order to keep the army supplied during the Civil War		
C	War Communism was brought in so that Lenin could control the countryside and the supply of food		
D	One consequence of War Communism was serious food shortages in 1920		
E	War Communism led to the death of seven million people during the famine of 1920		
F	War Communism was brought in because it followed the communist idea of central control and direction of the economy		

How do I build an answer?

Step 1
Choose two of the effects you have identified in Activity 2.

Step 2
Begin each paragraph with the effect and then fully explain it. Aim to write one extended paragraph on each effect.

Step 3

The best answers make links, explaining how one effect led to or is linked to the next. Signpost this by using the word 'link'. Link words or connectives would also help, such as *furthermore, in addition, this meant that, as a result of this, moreover.*

Step 4

Write a conclusion in which you summarise your two effects and reinforce the links between them.

Activity 3: Plan your answer

Explain the effects of Stalin's purges in the Soviet Union in the 1930s. (8)

Complete the following grid to plan your answer to this question using the advice in the **How do I build an answer?** section above.

First effect	Give the effect
Explanation	Explain it
Link	Make a link to the second effect. Remember the link words: *furthermore, in addition, this meant that, as a result of this, moreover.*
Second effect	Give the effect
Explanation	Explain it
Conclusion	Summarise the two effects and reinforce the links between them

Activity 4: Planning an answer

1. The following extracts make up an answer to the question below. Put them into the correct order, using the planning grid below.

Explain the effects of Lenin's return in April 1917. (8)

Extract A

This was because Lenin made it clear to his followers that he would not support the Provisional Government and that he wanted a workers' revolution. His plans were set out on the day of his return and were known as the April Theses. He made a number of speeches in which he gave simple slogans such as 'Peace, Land and Bread' and 'All Power to the Soviets'. These were easily understood by the Russian people.

Extract B

Overall, Lenin's return to Russia led to Bolshevik opposition to the Provisional Government which, in turn, encouraged greater support for the Bolsheviks as well as for the idea of revolution.

Extract C

The first consequence of Lenin's return to Russia in April 1917 was that it encouraged Bolshevik opposition to the Provisional Government.

Extract D

This increased support for the Bolsheviks was mainly due to Lenin's decision to oppose the war as well as his tremendous energy and vitality. His commitment to revolution spurred on the Bolsheviks. By June 1917 there were more than 40 newspapers spreading Lenin's views and ideas across Russia and there were 10,000 members of the Bolshevik Red Guard by June.

Extract E

As well as Lenin's return encouraging opposition to the Provisional Government, it also increased the possibility of a revolution as more people supported the Bolsheviks.

Extract F

Therefore, a second consequence of Lenin's return to Russia was that it encouraged greater support for the Bolsheviks.

	Extract (A, B, C, D, E or F)
First explained effect	
Link to second effect	
Second explained effect	
Conclusion	

2. On a separate piece of paper, plan and write an answer to the folowing question.

Explain the effects of Stalin's policy of collectivisation on the Soviet Union. (8)

> **Remember**
> You need to:
> o fully explain two effects
> o show links between the two effects.

Question 1(d)

Question 1(d) is a causation question (see page 23).

Activity 1: Understanding the exam question

Explain why Stalin became leader of the Soviet Union. (8)

1. Look at the marks for this question. How much would you expect to write in your answer? Ring your choice.
   - Two sentences
   - Two/three paragraphs
   - Three/four paragraphs

2. How long do you think you should spend answering this question? Ring your choice.
   - 6 minutes
   - 12 minutes
   - 18 minutes

3. a Underline the command word in the question.
   b Highlight key words such as dates, events or people.

4. Now decide what the question is asking you to do. Ring your choice.
   - Explain causation
   - Describe what happened
   - Explain consequence

Activity 2: Understanding the exam question

One important skill in answering 1(d) questions is selecting what is relevant to the question. The best answers focus on causation rather than simply listing everything about the particular event.

Look at the factors in the table below and:

- tick the two reasons you would use in your answer to the question in Activity 1
- put a cross next to those which you would not use in an answer to the question
- briefly explain why you have decided each reason is relevant or not relevant.

Factor	Relevant? ✓ or ✗	Explanation
Stalin's position as General Secretary		
The first Five-Year Plan		
Trotsky missed Lenin's funeral		
The Show Trials		
Collectivisation		

Activity 3: Using the mark scheme

Read the following answer to the question in Activity 1.

Student answer

Stalin was able to become leader of the Soviet Union because he was able to discredit Trotsky. For example, he made Trotsky look disloyal by tricking him into not attending Lenin's funeral. This is an example of the sort of cunning that Stalin showed in tricking people into thinking that Stalin's opponents were not suitable to run the country. So they supported him.

A second reason Stalin was able to become leader was his position as General Secretary of the Communist Party.

What mark would you give this answer? Tick the box in the Checklist table below. Give a brief explanation for your choice.

Checklist	Mark	Tick
Two developed statements	5	
One explained cause	6–7	
Two explained causes	7–8	
Links or prioritises the causes	8	

Explanation ....

....

Activity 4: Improve an answer

This answer could be improved by linking the two causes or by prioritising the causes.

1. Which of the following answers would **link** the two causes? Explain your choice(s).

A	Another reason that Stalin became leader was because he was underestimated by his rivals such as Trotsky.
B	Stalin was able to discredit Trotsky by taking advantage of his position as General Secretary which was the second reason he became leader.
C	Stalin cleverly played off his rivals against each other. For example he knew that Kamenev and Zinoviev feared Trotsky.

I would choose ...... because ....

2. Which of the following answers **prioritise** the causes? Explain your choice.

A	The most important reason why Stalin became leader of the Soviet Union was his position as General Secretary because this enabled him to greatly strengthen his own position in the Party.
B	Discrediting Trotsky and using his position as General Secretary were both important reasons why Stalin came to power.

C	Stalin's position as General Secretary was more important than discrediting Trotsky.

I would choose ... because ....

3. Which of the following extracts would either **improve or not improve** the answer? Explain each decision.

	Student answers	Improve? ✓/X	Explanation
A	In 1925 Stalin worked closely with Zinoviev and Kamenev and forced Trotsky to resign as Commissar of War. In 1926 Stalin worked with Bukharin and the right wing of the Communist Party against Zinoviev, Kamenev and Trotsky. In 1927, Trotsky was expelled from the party.		
B	He used his position as General Secretary to appoint officials who supported him and to influence party propaganda. He also used this position to remove known supporters of Trotsky and his other rivals to build up a power base. Stalin soon commanded the support of most party officials.		
C	Stalin promoted 'Socialism in One Country' which won popular support within the Communist Party as a contrast to Trotsky's idea of 'World Revolution'.		

Activity 5: Plan and write an answer

Explain why Lenin agreed to the terms of the Treaty of Brest-Litovsk. (8)

1. Plan an answer to this question in the grid below.

First explained reason	
Link to second reason	
Second explained reason	
Conclusion – prioritise the reasons	

2. Now write your answer on a separate piece of paper.

Question 2(a)

Question 2(a) is about process – the way in which something happened – or about change (see page 24).

Activity 1: Understanding the exam question

Explain how the Bolsheviks overcame opposition to their rule in the years 1917–24. (8)

1. How long do you think you should spend answering an 8-mark question? Ring your choice.
   - 6 minutes
   - 12 minutes
   - 18 minutes

2. How much do you think you're expected to write in that time? Ring your choice.
   - Two sentences
   - One paragraph
   - Two/three paragraphs

3. a Underline the command word in the question.
   b Highlight key words such as dates, events or people.

4. Decide what the question is asking you to do. Ring your choice.
   - Explain causation
   - Explain how something happened
   - Explain consequence

Remember
In question 2 there are 3 additional marks available for spelling, punctuation and grammar. Pay careful attention to these (see page 63).

Activity 2: Understanding the exam question

Look at the four different events below.

Highlight in green those which are relevant to this question.

The Civil War
The February Revolution
The April Theses
The Cheka

How do I build an answer?

Step 1
Select two of the events you have identified in Activity 2.

Step 2
Begin each paragraph with the way each event developed and then fully explain it. Aim to write two or three sentences on each way.

Step 3
The best answers make links, explaining how one way led to or is linked to the next. Signpost this by using the word 'link'. Link words or connectives would also help, such as *furthermore, in addition, this meant that, as a result of this, moreover.*

Step 4
Write a conclusion. Summarise your two ways and reinforce the links between them.

Hint
Focus on the question. It is about the way things developed so make sure you write about those ways. Do not just tell the story.

Explain how the Bolsheviks overcame opposition to their rule in the years 1917–24. (8)

Complete the following grid to plan your answer to this question using the advice in the **How do I build an answer?** section above.

First way	Give the way
Explanation	Explain it
Link	Make a link to the second way. Remember the link words: *furthermore, in addition, this meant that, as a result of this, moreover.*
Second way	Give the way
Explanation	Explain it
Conclusion	Summarise the two ways and reinforce the links between them

Question 2(b)

Question 2(b) is also about process or change (see page 24).

Activity 1: Understanding the exam question

Explain how the Provisional Government lost support during 1917. (8)

Read the following student answers to the question on page 56 and tick those which focus on the idea of **change**.

	Student answers	Tick
A	The Provisional Government was set up on 3 March 1917 and it promised to bring reforms to Russia. It also promised elections for a Constituent Assembly.	
B	The Provisional Government decided to continue with the war. This action made the Provisional Government unpopular with all those people who suffered as a result of the war.	
C	The Provisional Government faced a number of problems as soon as it was formed. Soldiers were deserting and peasants were looting the property of landlords.	
D	The Provisional Government failed to improve the food supplies because of the needs of war. The Provisional Government lost support as daily rations continued to fall.	
E	The Provisional Government failed to introduce changes such as land reform and this made them unpopular with many of the peasants.	

Activity 2: Using the mark scheme

Explain how Stalin dealt with the ethnic minorities in the Soviet Union in the 1930s. (8)

Level	Mark	Descriptor
2	3–5	**Developed statements of change** One or more statements are made, supported with relevant contextual knowledge
3	6–8	**Developed explanation of change** One or more changes are explained, supported by selected knowledge

Which level would you put the following answer in? Use the mark scheme above and explain your decision.

Student answer
One way Stalin dealt with ethnic minorities was that at first he supported the idea of local identity and was happy to have his photograph taken with people in national dress. He stressed the equality of the republics in the Soviet Union and encouraged local languages.
This is a Level .... answer because ....

Activity 3: Improve an answer

1. Which of the following would **improve or not improve** the answer? Explain each decision.

	Student answers	Improve? ✔ or ✘	Explanation
A	The Soviet government carried out 'ethnic cleansing' operations in border regions. Finnish, Latvian and Estonian families were deported from the Leningrad region to Kazakhstan and Siberia. At the same time families of Polish and German origin were deported from the border district of Kiev.		
B	Although Stalin was from the non-Russian state of Georgia, he had no sympathy for the plight of the many non-Russian groups which had suffered persecution and Russification under the Tsar.		
C	Stalin's policy towards the ethnic minorities changed as he became more worried about opposition. He was very concerned about opposition to collectivisation, much of which had come from the regions. So from 1932 Stalin introduced a policy of Russification – making people behave like Russians such as making Russian a compulsory second language in all schools.		

2. Which of the following would **link** the two changes in the answer? Explain your choice(s).

A	At first Stalin dealt with the ethnic minorities in a positive way to try to encourage support for his regime.
B	One way that Stalin dealt with the minorities was through a policy of Russification.
C	This positive way in which Stalin dealt with minorities changed as he became more worried about opposition and led to a policy of Russification.

I would choose ...... because ....
....

Activity 4: Plan and write an answer

Explain how the First World War affected Tsarist rule in 1917. (8)

1. Plan an answer to this question in the grid below.

First explained way	
Link to second way	
Second explained way	
Conclusion – link the ways	

2. Now write a full answer to the question on a separate piece of paper.

Question 3

Question 3 is a scaffolding question (see page 25).

Activity 1: Understanding the exam question

Was the opposition of peasants and town workers the main reason why the Tsar was forced to abdicate in 1917? Explain your answer. (16)

You may use the following in your answer and any other information of your own.
- Opposition of peasants and town workers
- Russia's poor performance in the First World War
- The weaknesses of Tsar Nicholas II
- The events in Petrograd in January and February 1917

1. Look at the marks for this question. How much would you expect to write in your answer? Ring your choice.
   - Two sentences
   - One paragraph
   - Three paragraphs
   - Four or more paragraphs

2. How long do you think you should spend answering this question? Ring your choice.
   - 10 minutes
   - 15 minutes
   - 25 minutes

Remember

Remember that you should leave time at the end to check your spelling, punctuation and grammar, as there are 4 additional marks available for these in question 3 (see page 63).

Activity 2: What is the question about?

1. Which of the following should you include in your answer? Underline your choice(s).
   - Brief points on the scaffolding factors
   - Developed statements on two or more of the factors
   - Explanation of at least two of the factors
   - Judgements on the importance of at least three of the factors

2. What is the focus of the question? Ring your choice.
   - Reasons for the abdication of the Tsar in 1917
   - Reasons for the Bolshevik Revolution of 1917
   - Reasons for the Bolshevik victory in the Civil War

Remember

Ensure you focus on the actual question. What is it asking you to do? It is not asking you to write as much as you know about the factors but to emphasise supported judgements on these factors (or others of your own) showing how they interacted.

How do I build an answer?

Step 1 First scaffolding point
Begin by writing a paragraph on the factor mentioned in the question, which will also be the first scaffolding point. Explain its importance and support this with your own knowledge.

Step 2 Further scaffolding points
Next, write a paragraph on each of the other scaffolding points. Explain the importance of each and support this with your own knowledge.

Step 3 Conclusion
You could begin with the word 'overall'. In your conclusion, explain how each of the factors is important by showing the links or relationship between them.

Activity 3: Writing your conclusion

1. Write notes about the four factors in the boxes.

2. For your conclusion, you have to explain why most, if not all, of the four factors were important and how they combined. In other words, the interrelationship or links between the factors in bringing about the event, or how the factors were dependent on one another. On the mind map:
   - draw lines to show links between the factors
   - on these lines, briefly explain how the two factors were linked or dependent on each other. One example has been done for you.

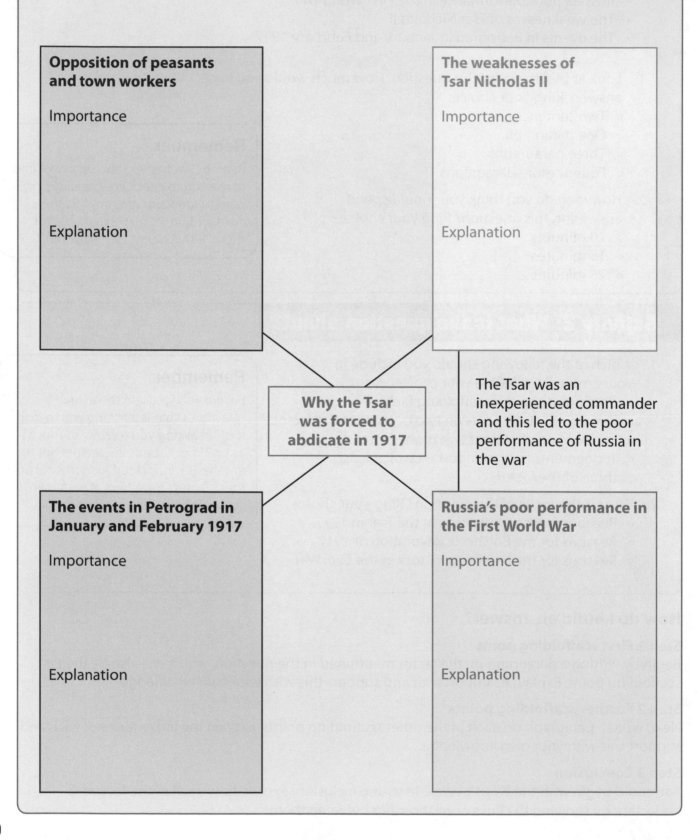

Opposition of peasants and town workers

Importance

Explanation

The weaknesses of Tsar Nicholas II

Importance

Explanation

Why the Tsar was forced to abdicate in 1917

The Tsar was an inexperienced commander and this led to the poor performance of Russia in the war

The events in Petrograd in January and February 1917

Importance

Explanation

Russia's poor performance in the First World War

Importance

Explanation

Activity 4: Using the mark scheme

Level	Mark	Descriptor
3	9–12	**Developed explanation of causation** ○ 9–10 marks for explaining two or more of the factors ○ 11–12 marks for explaining two or more of the factors and reaching a judgement on why one is more important than one other
4	13–16	**A sustained argument** This means the answer focuses throughout on the relative importance of the factors. ○ 13–14 marks for making judgements on the relative importance of more than two of the factors ○ 15–16 marks for showing the relative importance of all of the factors and illustrating that 'one most important reason' on its own could not provide a satisfactory explanation

1. What level would you give the following answer? Give reasons for your decision.

Student answer

Russia's poor performance in the war was an important reason for the abdication of the Tsar. By 1917 things were getting really bad in Russia. The war was not going at all well and there were heavy casualties and lots of desertions. The Russian army was poorly supplied and communications were weak. The Tsar had decided to put himself in charge of the army, so he took the blame. Obviously, if the Tsar was being blamed for the disaster that was the war, then there would be more support for those people trying to overthrow him. Another important factor was the opposition of peasants and town workers. Conditions in the countryside had always been poor and the peasants had pretty awful lives. Starvation was not uncommon. As Russia began to modernise, many people moved into towns to work in factories. Here they met conditions that were just as grim. They lived in hostels and worked long hours for poor pay. Living and working in such conditions increased their discontent and drove many of them to join radical groups opposing the Tsar.

Events in Petrograd were also important. In February 1917 there was a severe wave of strikes and soldiers refused to obey orders to fire on the strikers and demonstrators. The soldiers were mostly ex-peasants, so it is not surprising the authorities lost control in this way. As the authorities lost control, so those who opposed the Tsar were more likely to demonstrate or support groups like the Petrograd Soviet.

Overall, the most important reason for the abdication of the Tsar was Russia's poor performance in the war because this was blamed on the Tsar, who was the commander-in-chief of the armed forces.

Level:	Reason:

2. Suggest two improvements to this answer.

First improvement	
Second improvement	

Activity 5: Plan and write an answer

Was the inefficiency of Soviet industry the greatest problem Stalin had to face in the years 1924–39? Explain your answer. (16)

You may use the following in your answer and any other information of your own.
- The inefficiency of Soviet industry
- Opposition from Trotsky
- The Kulaks
- Harsh living and working conditions in towns

1. Plan an answer to the question by writing notes in the grid.

The first problem	Explain the problem of inefficiency in Soviet industry Make a judgement on its importance
The second problem	Explain the problem caused by a second scaffolding point Make a judgement on its importance
The third problem	Explain the problem caused by a third scaffolding point Make a judgement on its importance
The fourth problem	Explain the problem caused by a fourth scaffolding point Make a judgement on its importance
Conclusion	Make a judgement on the relative importance of all four problems, showing how they combined

2. Now write your full answer on a separate piece of paper. Make sure you are careful to spell and punctuate correctly and use grammar well, and check your answer over once you've finished.

Spelling, punctuation and grammar

In both question 2 and question 3 of Unit 2, the additional marks for spelling, punctuation and grammar are awarded across three levels. These are shown in the mark scheme on page 19.

Now let's look at some examples. Read the extracts below from three student answers to the question on page 59 and:

○ circle any spelling mistakes

○ underline any errors of punctuation or grammar

○ decide what level you think each answer should be in and write it next to the answer.

	Student answer	Level
A	One important reason for the abdication of the Tsar was the opposition of peasants and town workers. Conditions in the countryside had always been poor and the peasants had generally terrible living conditions and there was much starvation. There were also poor conditions for town workers. They lived in hostels and worked long hours for poor pay. These conditions encouraged peasants and town workers to join groups who opposed the Tsar such as the Social Revolutionaries. Another important reason for the abdication of the Tsar were the defeats suffered by the Russian armed forces in the war. More and more soldiers dezerted and returned to Russia because the Russian army was so poorly supplied and communications were weak. Nicholas II had made the mistake of making himself the commander-in-chief of the Russian armed forces. He was therefore blamed for the defeats.	
B	Events in Petrigrad were also important as a reason for the abdication of Nicolas II. In early March 1917 there was a severe wave of strikes and soldier's refused to obey orders to fire on the strikers and deminstrators. The soldiers' were mostly ex-peasants, so it is not surprising the authorities lost control in this way. As the authorities lost control so those who opposed the Tsar were more likely to demonstrate or support groups like the Petrograd Soviet. Another reason the Tsar abdicated was because the war was going badly. They're were heavy casualties and lots of desertions. The russian army was poorly supplied and communications was weak.	
C	By 1917 things were getting really bad in russia. the war was not going at all well there was alot of cassualtys and lots of desertions, The russian army was poorly surplied and comunications was weak. the Tsar had decided to put himself in charge of the army so he took lots of blame. Events in Petrigrad were also important, In early March 1917 their were a severe wave of strikes and sholdiers refused to obey orders to fire on the strikers. the sholdiers were mostly ex-pheasants, so it isn't suprising the authority's lost control in this way.	

Option 2C: The USA 1919–41

Question 1(a)

Question 1(a) is an inference question (see page 20).

Activity 1: Understanding the exam question

Source A is about women in the USA in the 1930s. Read the source and the exam question, and then answer the questions that follow.

Source A: From a history of the USA in the 20th century, published in 1994.

> The average pay for women in 1937 was $325, compared to $1,027 for men. The situation for black women was worse: 40% of black women worked, but for lower wages than white women. The New Deal offered little to women. The National Industrial Recovery Act of 1933 included Codes which set minimum wages and prices. They also set maximum working hours in industry. About a quarter of these Codes actually required women to be paid less than men. Only 8,000 women were employed by the Civilian Conservation Corps out of the 2.75 million people involved in the scheme.

What can you learn from Source A about the position of women in the USA in the 1930s? (4)

This question is worth 4 marks.

1. How long would you expect an answer to be? Ring your choice.
   - Two sentences
   - One paragraph
   - Two paragraphs

2. Approximately how long should you spend answering this question? Ring your choice.
   - 2 minutes
   - 6 minutes
   - 10 minutes

3. What is the question asking you to do? Ring your choice.
   - Make inferences from the source
   - Make supported inferences from the source
   - Summarise the source

Activity 2: Mark an answer

What mark would you give the following student answers to the question in Activity 1? Use the mark scheme to help you decide.

Level	Mark	Descriptor
1	1	Students do no more than copy/paraphrase the source.
2	2–3	**Makes unsupported inferences** Inference given but not supported by source ○ 2 marks for one unsupported inference ○ 3 marks for two unsupported inferences
3	4	**Makes supported inferences** Inference given and it is supported by the source, e.g. 'because the source tells me…' One well-supported inference can be sufficient.

	Student answers	Mark
A	Women were treated as second-class citizens in the USA in the 1930s.	
B	I can learn that the New Deal did very little for women. This is because the source says that out of 2.75 million employed by the Civilian Conservation Corps, only 8,000 were women.	
C	I can learn that women were not treated as well as men. We are told that their pay was $325 a year compared to $1,027 for men	
D	We can learn that the New Deal offered very little to women. The National Industrial Recovery Act of 1933 included Codes which set minimum wages and prices. They also set maximum working hours in industry.	
E	Women were paid poorly compared to men.	

Activity 3: Improving an answer

Here is an answer which is an unsupported inference. Improve this answer by writing below how this inference is supported by the source.

I can learn that women in the USA were second-class citizens in the 1930s.

Activity 4: Making a supported inference

Source B: From a history of the USA, published in 2009.

Conditions worsened in the Dust Bowl in 1935–36. 'Black Blizzards' blew harder, for longer, and came more often. In 1936 rain came – heavy rain that flooded many places and swept away much of the remaining topsoil. Hundreds of thousands of people had left to become migrant workers in other states. They travelled around, by car or on foot, to work on the seasonal crops. The Farm Security Administration set up more permanent camps after 1937.

What can you learn from Source B about farming in the USA in the mid-1930s? (4)

Answer this question by completing the sentences below.

This source suggests that..

....

I know that because the source says..

....

....

Question 1(b)

Question 1(b) is a describe question (see page 21).

Activity 1: Understanding the exam question

Describe the system of mass production used by the Ford Motor Company. (6)

1. Look at the marks for this question. How much would you expect to write in your answer? Ring your choice.
   - Two sentences
   - Two/three paragraphs
   - Three/four paragraphs

2. How long do you think you should spend answering this question? Ring your choice.
   - 10 minutes
   - 15 minutes
   - 20 minutes

3. a Underline the word in the question which is telling you what to do, the 'command' word.

   b Highlight key words such as dates, events or people.

4. Now decide what the question is asking you to do. Ring your choice.
   - Explain causation
   - Describe what happened
   - Explain consequence

Activity 2: Mark an answer

Read the answer below to the question in Activity 1.

- **First** highlight in blue any simple statements.
- **Next** highlight in green any supporting details.
- **Then** using the mark scheme below, decide what mark to give the answer and tick the column in the Checklist.
- **Finally** give a brief explanation for your choice.

> **Student answer**
>
> Mass production was about people working in factories. In this system each man had a specific task and stood on a production line as the cars came by. If your job was to put on a wheel, then you just did that. You did not make whole cars. Mass production was a much more efficient method of manufacturing goods.

Level	Mark	Descriptor
2	4–6	**Developed statement(s)** Simple statements with additional supporting material. • 4–5 marks for one developed statement • 5–6 marks for two or more developed statements

Hint

Using the words 'for example' often means that the statement has been supported.

Checklist	Mark	Tick
One developed statement	4	
One well-developed statement	5	
Two developed statements	6	

Explanation ....

....

Activity 3: Improve an answer

Which of the following statements would improve the answer in Activity 2? Explain your choice.

	Possible additional statements	Tick
A	Henry Ford was also prepared to use modern advertising techniques to sell his cars. For example, he realised the value of using attractive women in adverts, not only because it would encourage men to buy cars, but also to promote the idea of female drivers.	
B	This was because the workers did not have to waste time walking round fetching tools and equipment. The tools and equipment were brought to them. As a result, a great deal of time was saved.	
C	Mass production was also about producing goods, such as cars, at a faster rate.	
I chose .... because		

Activity 4: Plan and write an answer

1. Plan an answer to the following question.

Describe the lifestyle of a 'flapper' in the USA in the 1920s. (6)

The first lifestyle point was	
Describe it	
The second lifestyle point was	
Describe it	

2. Now write a full answer to this question on a separate piece of paper.

Question 1(c)

Question 1(c) is a consequence question (see page 22).

Activity 1: Understanding the exam question

Explain the effects of the Wall Street Crash on the USA in the years 1929–32. (8)

1. How long do you think you should spend answering an 8-mark question? Ring your choice.
   - 6 minutes
   - 12 minutes
   - 18 minutes

2. How much do you think you're expected to write in that time? Ring your choice.
   - Two sentences
   - Two/three paragraphs
   - Three/four paragraphs

Activity 2: Understanding the exam question

Identify which of the following are causes and which are effects of the Wall Street Crash. Tick the correct column.

		Cause	Effect
A	The Wall Street Crash was partly due to overproduction in the US economy		
B	One consequence of the Wall Street Crash was the collapse of many American banks		
C	One consequence of the Wall Street Crash was that it brought poverty to the USA		
D	The Wall Street Crash was also due to over-speculation on the American stock market		
E	Another consequence of the Wall Street Crash was that there was a massive rise in unemployment		
F	The Wall Street Crash also happened because people very quickly lost confidence in the stock market		

How do I build an answer?

Step 1
Choose two of the effects you have identified in Activity 2.

Step 2
Explain each effect fully. Begin each paragraph with the effect and then fully explain it.
Aim to write a good length paragraph on each effect.

Step 3
The best answers make links. This means explaining how one effect led to or is linked to the next. Signpost this by using the word 'link'. Link words or connectives would help, such as *furthermore, in addition, this meant that, as a result of this, moreover.*

Step 4
Write a conclusion in which you summarise your two effects and reinforce the links between them.

Activity 3: Plan your answer

Explain the effects of the Wall Street Crash on the USA in the years 1929–32. (8)

Complete the following grid to plan your answer to this question using the advice in the **How do I build an answer?** section above.

First effect	Give the effect
Explanation	Explain it
Link	Make a link to the second effect. Remember the link words: *furthermore, in addition, this meant that, as a result of this, moreover.*
Second effect	Give the effect
Explanation	Explain it
Conclusion	Summarise the two effects and reinforce the links between them

Activity 4: Planning an answer

The following extracts make up an answer to the question below. Put them into the correct order, using the planning grid.

Explain the effects of Prohibition in the USA in the 1920s. (8)

Extract A

> Overall the main consequence of the introduction of Prohibition was to encourage the growth of rival gangs who were prepared to provide illegal alcohol, leading to the second consequence, the smuggling of moonshine from abroad.

Extract B

> The first consequence of Prohibition was the breaking of the law by many Americans.

Extract C

> Moreover, these gangs were prepared to import this liquor from abroad, which led to the second consequence of introduction of Prohibition.

Extract D

> This alcohol, known as moonshine, was smuggled from Europe, Mexico, Canada and the Caribbean and was easily brought into the USA, which has 30,000 kilometres of coastal and land borders to guard.

Extract E

> This was because many Americans were prepared to break the law and drink alcohol. Gangs competed with each other to make fortunes from the production, buying and selling of this illegal alcohol. One example was the gang led by Al Capone in Chicago. These rival gangs also set up speakeasies. These were illegal bars where people could drink alcohol. In New York alone there were more than 30,000 speakeasies by 1929.

Extract F

> This second consequence was the smuggling of illegal liquor into America, often by organised gangs.

Planning grid

	Extract (A, B, C, D, E or F)
First explained effect	
Link to second effect	
Second explained effect	
Conclusion	

Activity 5: Plan and write an answer

On a separate piece of paper, plan and write an answer to the following question.

Explain the effects of the 'roaring twenties' on women in the USA. (8)

Remember

You need to:
- fully explain two effects
- show links between the two effects.

Question 1(d)

Question 1(d) is a causation question (see page 23).

Activity 1: Understanding the exam question

Explain why organised crime grew in the USA in the 1920s. (8)

1. Look at the marks for this question. How much would you expect to write in your answer? Ring your choice.
   - Two sentences
   - Two/three paragraphs
   - Three/four paragraphs

2. How long do you think you should spend answering this question? Ring your choice.
   - 6 minutes
   - 12 minutes
   - 18 minutes

3. a Underline the command word.

   b Highlight key words such as dates, events or people.

4. Decide what the question is asking you to do. Ring your choice.
   - Explain causation
   - Describe what happened
   - Explain consequence

Activity 2: Understanding the exam question

One important skill in answering 1(d) questions is selecting what is relevant to the question. The best answers focus on causation rather than simply listing everything about the event.

Look at the factors in the table below.
- Tick the two reasons you would use in your answer to the question in Activity 1.
- Put a cross next to those which you would not use in an answer to the question.
- Briefly explain why you have decided each reason is relevant or not relevant.

Factor	Relevant? ✔ or ✘	Explanation
Opportunities to make money		
Growth of the car industry		
The Sacco and Vanzetti case		
Prohibition		
The Monkey Trial		

Activity 3: Using the mark scheme

Read the following answer to the question in Activity 1.

Student answer

Organised crime grew in the USA in the 1920s because there were opportunities to make money. In particular, this was the result of the introduction of Prohibition. People were not allowed to drink and so speakeasies were set up by gangsters where alcohol could be bought. This was such a lucrative business that it was the gangs which controlled the speakeasies. As profits grew, so did organised crime to try to keep control of the share the gangs had. Organised crime also grew because of the corruption of many public officials.

What mark would you give this answer? Tick the box in the Checklist table below. Give a brief explanation for your choice.

Checklist	Mark	Tick
Two developed statements	5	
One explained cause	6–7	
Two explained causes	7–8	
Links or prioritises the causes	8	

Explanation ....

....

Activity 4: Improve an answer

This answer could be improved by linking the two causes or by prioritising the causes.

1. Which of the following answers would **link** the two causes? Explain your choice(s).

A	Another reason for the growth of organised crime was corruption.
B	These profits from of the illegal sale of alcohol gave gangsters the money to bribe corrupt officials, which was the second reason for the growth of organised crime, corruption.
C	Organised crime was due to the introduction of Prohibition and the bribery of public officials

I would choose ...... because ....

2. Which of the following answers **prioritise** the causes? Explain your choice.

A	The most important reason for the growth of organised crime was the introduction of Prohibition which meant that gangs could make a fortune from the sale of illegal alcohol and used their profits to bribe public officials.
B	The introduction of Prohibition and the corruption of public officials were both important reasons for the growth of organised crime.

C	The introduction of Prohibition was more important than the corruption of public officials.

I would choose … because ....

3. Which of the following extracts would either **improve or not improve** the answer? Explain each decision.

	Student answers	Improve? ✓/✗	Explanation
A	Organised crime also grew because Prohibition was impossible to enforce. There were not enough enforcement agents to stop the sale of illegal alcohol.		
B	Al Capone was one of the most famous gangsters of the time. He was given the nickname 'Scarface' following a fight that broke out when he was working as a bouncer at a New York club. He moved to Chicago where he eventually controlled speakeasies, bookmakers' joints, gambling houses, nightclubs and breweries. He was also the first person to open soup kitchens in 1929.		
C	Police, city officials and federal agents were aware of the spread of speakeasies and the sale of illegal alcohol but were prepared to turn a blind eye to the growth of organised crime and their control of the illegal trade in alcohol in return for backhanders. Al Capone's influence in Chicago grew because he controlled the mayor and the senior police officer and fixed local elections.		

Activity 5: Plan and write an answer

Explain why there was opposition to Roosevelt's New Deal. (8)

1. Plan an answer to this question in the grid below.

First explained reason	
Link to second reason	
Second explained reason	
Conclusion – prioritise the reasons	

2. Now write your answer on a separate piece of paper.

Question 2(a)

Question 2(a) is about process – the way in which something happened – or about change (see page 24).

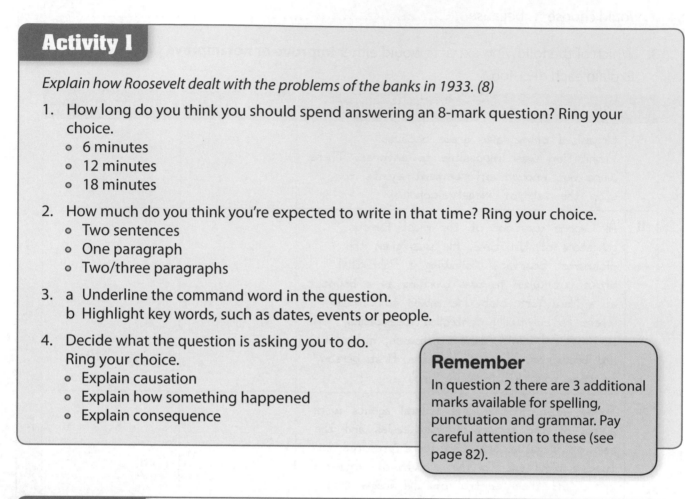

Activity 1

Explain how Roosevelt dealt with the problems of the banks in 1933. (8)

1. How long do you think you should spend answering an 8-mark question? Ring your choice.
    o 6 minutes
    o 12 minutes
    o 18 minutes

2. How much do you think you're expected to write in that time? Ring your choice.
    o Two sentences
    o One paragraph
    o Two/three paragraphs

3. a Underline the command word in the question.
    b Highlight key words, such as dates, events or people.

4. Decide what the question is asking you to do. Ring your choice.
    o Explain causation
    o Explain how something happened
    o Explain consequence

Remember

In question 2 there are 3 additional marks available for spelling, punctuation and grammar. Pay careful attention to these (see page 82).

Activity 2

Look at the four different events below.

Highlight in green those which are relevant to this question.

The Emergency Banking Act of 1933
The Civilian Conservation Corps
The National Industrial Recovery Act
Roosevelt's Fireside Chats

How do I build an answer?

Step 1
Select two of the ways you have identified in Activity 2.

Step 2
Begin each paragraph with a way and then fully explain it. Aim to write two or three sentences on each way.

Hint

Focus on the question. It is about ways in which things developed so ensure you write about these ways. Do not just tell the story.

Step 3

The best answers make links, explaining how one way led to or is linked to the next. Signpost this by using the word 'link'. Link words or connectives would also help, such as *furthermore, in addition, this meant that, as a result of this, moreover.*

Step 4

Write a conclusion. Summarise your two ways and reinforce the links between them.

Activity 3: Planning an answer

Explain how Roosevelt dealt with the problems of the banks in 1933. (8)

Complete the following grid to plan your answer to this question using the advice in the **How do I build an answer?** section above.

First way	Give the way
Explanation	Explain it
Link	Make a link to the second way. Remember the link words: *furthermore, in addition, this meant that, as a result of this, moreover.*
Second way	Give the way
Explanation	Explain it
Conclusion	Summarise the two ways and reinforce the links between them

Question 2(b)

Question 2(b) is also about process or change (see page 24).

Activity 1: Understanding the exam question

Explain how the lives of farmers changed in the years 1919–29. (8)

Tick the following student answers to the above question which focus on the idea of **change**.

	Student answers	Tick
A	The main reason for the growth of the farming industry during the First World War was the demand for food from Britain and France.	
B	Farmers became poorer because when the war was over many farmers could not get the high prices they had got during the war and their income declined.	
C	The Agricultural Credits Act was introduced in 1923 and set up twelve Federal Intermediate Credit banks which were allowed to lend money to farmers.	
D	The position of farmers grew worse because many lost land because they were unable to pay their mortgages.	
E	One of the worst changes was in the position of farm workers known as sharecroppers, many of whom became bankrupt in the 1920s.	

Activity 2: Using the mark scheme

Level	Mark	Descriptor
3	6–8	**Developed explanation of change** One or more changes are explained, supported by selected knowledge • 6–7 marks for one explained change • 7–8 marks for two or more explained changes • 8 marks for answers which prioritise changes or show links between them

What mark would you give this answer? Use the mark scheme above. Explain your choice.

Student answer
The first change in the position of the farmers was that they became much poorer in the 1920s. During the First World War they had sold their products overseas at a good price, especially to European countries which had not been able to produce enough food to feed their people. Many American farmers made good profits. However, when the war ended, there was much less demand in Europe and many farmers could not get such high prices and their profits fell. Another change was that some farmers lost their land because they could not pay their mortgages. This was because their profits had fallen.

I would give this .... marks because ....
....

Activity 3: Improve an answer

1. Which of the following would **link** the two changes in the answer? Explain your choice(s).

A	Another change was that many farmers could not pay their mortgages.
B	For the most part things got worse for American farmers in the 1920s because of the fall in demand and the failure to pay mortgages.
C	This fall in profits led to another change, the failure of a great number of farmers to pay the additional mortgages they had taken on in the First World War.

I would choose ...... because ....
....

2. Which of the following would **improve or not improve** the answer? Explain each decision.

	Student answers	Improve? ✔ or ✘	Explanation
A	The Agricultural Credits Act was introduced in 1923 to try to solve the problems in farming. It set up twelve Federal Intermediate Credit Banks which were allowed to lend money to farmers. In order to keep up their livelihood, farmers had to continue to produce food and try to sell it at a lower price.		
B	The position of black farmers changed. Many were sharecroppers in the Southern States who gave a share of their crop as rent. About one million black farm workers were unemployed by the end of the 1920s.		
C	During the First World War, many farmers had expanded their farms due to increased demand and taken on additional mortgages. As prices and profits fell in the 1920s they were unable to make the mortgage payments. As a result they switched from farming to sharecropping, or even gave up farming and moved to the cities to find work. Others moved to California to find work on fruit farms.		

Activity 4: Plan and write an answer

Explain how new consumer goods changed lives for many families in the USA in the 1920s. (8)

1. Plan an answer to this question in the grid below.

First explained change	
Link to second change	
Second explained change	
Conclusion – link the changes	

2. Now write a full answer to the question on a separate piece of paper.

Question 3

Question 3 is a scaffolding question (see page 25).

Activity 1: Understanding the exam question

Was motor car ownership the most important reason for improvements in the way of life for many Americans in the 1920s? Explain your answer. (16)

You may use the following in your answer and any other information of your own.
- Motor car ownership
- New consumer goods
- New forms of entertainment
- High levels of prosperity

1. Look at the marks for this question. How much would you expect to write in your answer? Ring your choice.
   - Two sentences
   - One paragraph
   - Three paragraphs
   - Four or more paragraphs

2. How long do you think you should spend answering this question? Ring your choice.
   - 10 minutes
   - 15 minutes
   - 25 minutes

Remember

In question 3 there are 4 additional marks available for spelling, punctuation and grammar. Pay careful attention to these (see page 82).

Activity 2: What is the question about?

1. Which of the following should you include in your answer?
   Underline your choice(s).
   - Brief points on the scaffolding factors
   - Developed statements on two or more of the factors
   - Explanation of at least two of the factors
   - Judgements on the importance of at least three of the factors

2. What is the focus of the question? Ring your choice.
   - The Wall Street Crash of 1929
   - The roaring twenties
   - Roosevelt's New Deal

Remember

Ensure you focus on the actual question. What is it asking you to do? It is not asking you to write as much as you know about the factors but to emphasise supported judgements on these factors (or others of your own), showing how they interacted.

How do I build an answer?

Step 1 First scaffolding point
Begin by writing a paragraph on the factor mentioned in the question, which will also be the first scaffolding point. Explain its importance and support this with your own knowledge.

Step 2 Further scaffolding points
Next, write a paragraph on each of the other scaffolding points. Explain the importance of each and support this with your own knowledge.

Step 3 Conclusion
You could begin with the word 'overall'. In your conclusion, explain how each of the factors is important by showing the links or relationship between them.

1. Write notes about the four factors in the boxes.

2. For your conclusion you have to explain why most, if not all, of the four factors were important and how they combined. In other words, the interrelationship or links between the factors in bringing about the event, or how the factors were dependent on each other. On the mind map:
   - draw lines to show links between the factors
   - on these lines, briefly explain how the two factors were linked or dependent on each other. One example has been done for you.

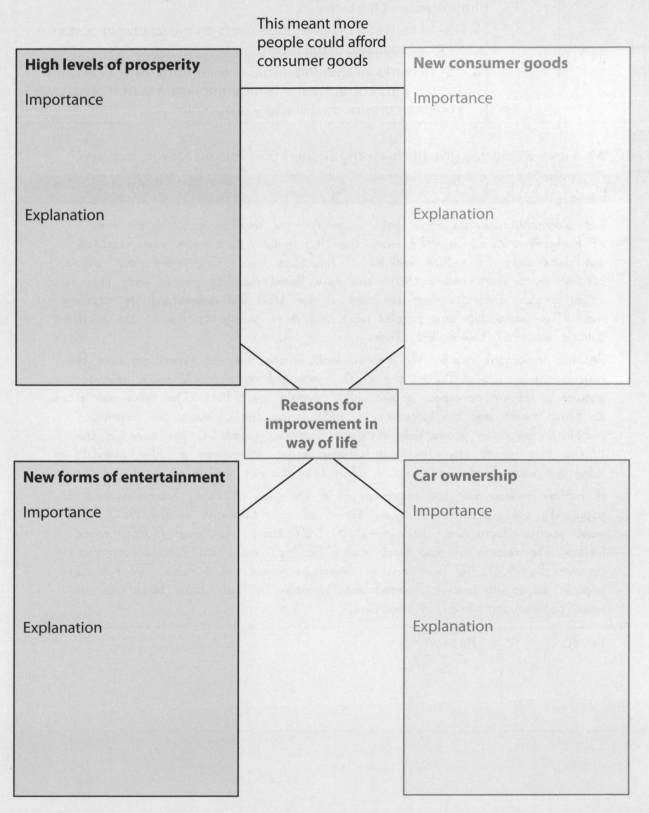

High levels of prosperity

Importance

Explanation

This meant more people could afford consumer goods

New consumer goods

Importance

Explanation

Reasons for improvement in way of life

New forms of entertainment

Importance

Explanation

Car ownership

Importance

Explanation

Activity 4: Using the mark scheme

Level	Mark	Descriptor
3	9–12	**Developed explanation of causation** ○ 9–10 marks for explaining two or more of the factors ○ 11–12 marks for explaining two or more of the factors and reach a judgement on why one is more important than one other
4	13–16	**A sustained argument** This means the answer focuses throughout on the relative importance of the factors. ○ 13–14 marks for making judgements on the relative importance of more than two of the factors ○ 15–16 marks for showing the relative importance of all of the factors and illustrate that 'one most important reason' on its own could not provide a satisfactory explanation

1. What level would you give the following answer? Give reasons for your decision.

Student answer

Car ownership was an important reason for the improvements in the lives of many Americans. In 1929 more than 4.5 million cars were manufactured and there were 27 million vehicles on American roads. This meant that people became much more mobile. With this new found mobility people were able to travel greater distances, see the rest of the USA and understand the country more. Car ownership also enabled more and more people to live in the healthier suburb areas of towns and cities.

Another important reason for improvement in the lives of Americans was the new consumer goods. During the 1920s more and more people were able to acquire a lot of consumer goods which changed their lives. They now had access to cheap radios and refrigerators, as well as vacuum cleaners and washing machines. American production of these goods increased 50 per cent in the 1920s. This meant that American citizens began to expect a higher standard of living and were ready to complain when they did not get it.

A further reason for the improvement in the lives of many Americans was the popularity and availability of many forms of entertainment in the 1920s. The most popular form was the cinema. By 1927 there were over 17,000 movie houses. The release of the first 'talkie' in 1927 made the cinema even more popular. By 1930, 40 per cent of American homes had a radio. Sport became popular, especially boxing, baseball and American football. Babe Ruth was the most popular sportsman of the time.

Level:	Reason:

2. Suggest two improvements to this answer.

First improvement	
Second improvement	

Activity 5: Plan and write an answer

Was unemployment the most serious problem in the USA in the 1930s? Explain your answer. (16)

You may use the following in your answer and any other information of your own.
- Unemployment
- Homelessness
- Lack of social security
- The depression in farming

1. Plan an answer to the question by writing notes in the grid.

The first problem	Explain the problem of unemployment Make a judgement on its importance
The second problem	Explain the problem caused by a second scaffolding point Make a judgement on its importance
The third problem	Explain the problem caused by a third scaffolding point Make a judgement on its importance
The fourth problem	Explain the problem caused by a fourth scaffolding point Make a judgement on its importance
Conclusion	Make a judgement on the relative importance of all four problems, showing how they combined

2. Now write your full answer on a separate piece of paper. Make sure you are careful to spell and punctuate correctly and use grammar well, and check your answer over once you've finished.

Spelling, punctuation and grammar

In both question 2 and question 3 of Unit 2, the additional marks for spelling, punctuation and grammar are awarded across three levels. These are shown in the mark scheme on page 19.

Now let's look at some examples. Read the extracts below from three student answers to the question on page 78 and:

o circle any spelling mistakes

o underline any errors of punctuation or grammar

o decide what level you think each answer should be in and write it next to the answer.

	Student answer	Level
A	One reason for the improvement in the lives of many Americans was the popularity and availability of many forms of entertainment in the 1920s. The most popular form was the cinema. By 1927 there were over 17,000 movie houses. The release of the first 'talkie' in 1927 made the cinema even more popular. By 1930 40 per cent of American homes had a radio. Sport became popular especially boxing, baseball and American football and babe Ruth was the most popular sportsman of the time. Another important reason for improvement in the lives of Americans was the new consumer goods. During the 1920's more and more people were able to acquire a lot of consumer goods which changed their lives. They now had access to cheap radios and refrigerators, as well as vacuum cleaners and washing machines. American production of these goods increased 50 per cent in the 1920s. This meant that American citizens began to expect a higher standard of living and were ready to complain when they did not get it.	
B	Another important reason for improvement in the lives of Americans was the new consumer goods. During the 1920's more and more people were able to acquire a lot of consumer goods which changed there lives, they now had access to cheap radios and refrigderators, as well as vacuum cleaners and washing machines. american production of these goods increased 50 per cent in the 1920s. This meant that american citizens began to expect a higher standard of living and were ready to complain when they did not get it. Car ownership was another important reason for the improvements in the life of many Americans. in 1929 more than 4.5 million cars were manufactured and there were 27 million vehicles on roads in the USA. This meant that people became much more mobile.	
C	There was alot of car ownership in the usa. in 1929 more than 4.5 million cars were builded. This meant that people could travel greater distences see the rest of the USA and understand the country more. Car ownership also alowed more and more people to live in the healthier suburb areas of towns and citties. Their was many forms of entertment in the 1920's. The most popular form was the cinema, by 1927 their was over 17,000 movie houses. by 1930 many american homes had a radio. Sport became popular especially boxing, baseball and american football. babe ruth was the most popular sportsman of the time.	

Unit 3: Modern World Source Enquiry

Introduction

What is Unit 3 about?

Unit 3 is a source enquiry unit. You will answer source questions on one of the following options. Highlight the option you have studied:

- Option 3A: War and the transformation of British society, c.1903–28 (pages 92–104)
- Option 3B: War and the transformation of British society, c.1931–51 (pages 105–117)
- Option 3C: A divided union? The USA 1945–70 (pages 118–130)

What do I need to know?

You have to answer five questions, each testing different source skills, including:

- making supported inferences (see page 87)
- explaining the message and purpose of a source (see page 88)
- cross-referencing three sources (see page 89)
- evaluating the utility or reliability of two sources (see page 90)
- using sources to test a hypothesis (see page 91).

You will also need to support these source skills with your own contextual knowledge. This means the knowledge that you have about the topic. This knowledge will help you with your source skills because:

- it will help you understand what the source is suggesting
- it will enable you to make judgements about the source itself – how accurate it is, how well it has covered the event.

Remember

Contextual knowledge does not involve a detailed knowledge of key events within an option. It requires an awareness and understanding of general developments that were taking place at that time. So don't panic if you have not studied a particular event or topic mentioned in the sources in the exam paper. Make use of your broader contextual knowledge as well as your source skills to answer the questions.

You have 75 minutes to answer this exam paper. It is worth 54 marks. As well as the exam paper, you will be given a source booklet with six sources (labelled A–F) on a topic within your option. They will be a mixture of written sources and illustrations. You have to answer five questions on these sources.

- Question 1 is an inference question on Source A and is worth 6 marks.

- Question 2 is a source analysis question on Source B and is worth 8 marks.

- Question 3 is a cross-referencing/comparison question on Sources A, B and C and is worth 10 marks.

- Question 4 will ask you to judge/evaluate **either** the utility **or** the reliability of Sources D and E and is worth 10 marks.

- Question 5 will give you a view (or 'hypothesis') and ask you to use the sources (all six if possible) and your contextual knowledge to judge how far they support and challenge the view. It is worth 16 marks plus an additional 4 marks for spelling, punctuation and grammar. The mark scheme below shows how these 4 marks are awarded across three levels.

0 marks	Errors severely hinder the meaning of the response or students do not spell, punctuate or use the rules of grammar within the context of the demands of the question.
Level 1: Threshold performance 1 mark	Students spell, punctuate and use the rules of grammar with reasonable accuracy in the context of the demands of the question. Any errors do not hinder meaning in the response. Where required, they use a limited range of specialist terms appropriately.
Level 2: Intermediate performance 2–3 marks	Students spell, punctuate and use the rules of grammar with considerable accuracy and general control of meaning in the context of the demands of the question. Where required, they use a good range of specialist terms with facility.
Level 3: High performance 4 marks	Students spell, punctuate and use the rules of grammar with consistent accuracy and effective control of meaning in the context of the demands of the question. Where required, they use a wide range of specialist terms adeptly and with precision.

Read the guidance on source skills and on how to answer each of these question types over the next seven pages. Then turn to the pages for the option you are studying:

- Pages 92–104 for Option 3A: War and the transformation of British society, c.1903–28

- Pages 105–117 for Option 3B: War and the transformation of British society, c.1931–51

- Pages 118–130 for Option 3C: A divided union? The USA 1945–70.

Source skills

You will need to make use of a variety of skills when you answer source questions. These include annotating sources, making use of the contents of sources and your contextual knowledge and understanding, as well as being able to apply the Nature, Origins and Purpose of sources. These are shown in the examples given below.

Annotating sources

First of all, read the question before you look at the relevant source or sources. This will ensure that you make full use of the source. You may find it useful to annotate the sources as you read them, by either highlighting or underlining the key points in the information given above the source, which is known as the provenance, for example, who produced the source and when and what type of source it is. In a written source, you should also highlight the key words or phrases in the source itself. In illustrations, you should also highlight the key features or people shown.

This will help you to work out what the source is suggesting.

Contents

This is the information which the source gives you about an event or person. You will need to identify information such as dates and actual events, as well as opinions and points of view. For example, in Source A on the next page you can see:

- Winston Churchill, the prime minister, in the foreground
- a catchy slogan
- tanks and fighter planes in the background.

Contextual knowledge

This means the knowledge that you have about a topic or event. This knowledge will help you with your source skills because:

- it will ensure that you understand what the source is suggesting
- it will enable you to make judgements about the source itself – how accurate it is, how well it has covered the event.

For example, looking again at Source A it would be helpful to know that the poster was produced during the Second World War, at a time when Britain was alone in facing Germany and Italy. Winston Churchill was popular with most British people because of his determination not to surrender.

Using the Nature, Origins and Purpose of sources

This tests your ability to make use of the provenance of the source and why the source was produced. You will use these skills in questions 2–5.

Source A: A poster issued by the British government in late 1940.

"LET US GO FORWARD TOGETHER"

Nature

This means the type of source. Is it a poster, photograph, cartoon, speech, diary, letter? This is a poster. Posters are usually produced for propaganda purposes, to persuade people to think or act in a certain way.

Origins

This means when the source was produced and by whom. This was produced by the British government in late 1940.

Purpose

This means, why was the source produced. What is it trying to make you do? Who is it trying to make you support? This is an example of a propaganda poster which is trying to get your support for the prime minister and the war effort, and to keep up the morale of the British people.

How do I answer question 1?

Question 1 is an **inference** question.

What is an inference?

Making an inference is when you work something out from what the source says. It is **not** simply repeating information in the source. It means:

- reading between the lines of what the source says to find out what it is suggesting about a person or event
- squeezing more information from the source than it actually tells you.

How will I be marked?

Question 1 is worth 6 marks. You have to make two supported inferences.

Making a supported inference means backing up your inference with information, possibly a quote, from the source.

In other words…

'In Year 9 at school, I mainly studied British history, which I found boring and hard. I achieved just over half marks in the end of year exam. In Year 10, I studied world history, which I found interesting and seemed easier to follow. I achieved over 70% in the end of year exam.'

Possible inferences	Possible support for inferences
The student greatly improved in history because he/she liked world history much more than British history	… because it says British history was boring and world history was interesting
British history is more difficult than world history	… because it says that British history was hard and world history was easy to follow
He/she greatly improved in history from Year 9 to Year 10	… because in Year 9 the student achieved just over half marks and in Year 10 over 70%

How do I answer question 2?

Question 2 is a **source analysis** question. It is asking you to explain the message and purpose of a source.

What is meant by the message of a source?

The message is what the source is suggesting about the person or event, what it is trying to make you think or believe about the person or event.

What is meant by the purpose of a source?

Purpose is distinct from message. Purpose is what the message is designed to achieve. Why was the source produced? What is it trying to make you do? Is it trying to get you to support or turn against a person or event? For example, speeches are usually made because the speaker wants to get the support of the audience.

In other words...

You often see adverts for cars in newspapers and magazines or on the television. The message of the advert is that the car is real value for money, has all the best features and plenty of room inside. The purpose of the advert is to persuade you to buy such a car.

How will I be marked?

This question is worth 8 marks. The mark scheme gives:

- 3–5 marks for supported statements which identify the message of the source and give details in support from:
  - the content of the source – what the source says or shows
  - the context of the source – using own knowledge about the circumstances in which the source was produced.
- 6–7 marks for explaining the content, context and purpose of the source analysing either the selection or treatment of content to explain purpose.
- 8 marks for analysing the selection and treatment of content to explain purpose.

Make sure your answer explains the purpose using both the contents and context of the source.

How do I answer question 3?

Question 3 is a **cross-referencing** question using three of the sources, Sources A, B and C.

What is meant by cross-referencing?

A cross-referencing question is asking you to compare the views given by three sources, A, B and C, about a particular event. Here are two examples of cross-referencing questions showing the possible wording used.

- How far do Sources A and B support the evidence of Source C about a particular event, an impression, view or attitude?
- How far do these sources agree about a particular event?

In the exam you will be asked to study three sources and show how they agree and disagree.

In other words...

You might compare different views of a sporting event, a pop concert or even a television programme, looking for similarities and differences.

For example, you might read two or three accounts in different newspapers of a football match, with ratings out of ten for the performance of the players. These accounts might have similarities and differences in their views of the game itself and their ratings of the players.

On the other hand, you might read two or three different reviews of a pop concert in magazines or newspapers, one of which says it was excellent, another gives it mixed reviews and the third suggests it was not very good. You may well make judgements on how much agreement or disagreement there is between these accounts.

How will I be marked?

This question is worth 10 marks. The mark scheme gives:

- 4–6 marks for supported statements showing agreement **or** disagreement between the sources
- 7 marks for supported statements showing agreement **and** disagreement between the sources
- 8–9 marks for a judgement on the degree of support between the sources using their contents **or** reliability
- 9–10 marks for a judgement on the degree of support between the sources using their contents **and** reliability.

Your answer needs to make judgements on the degree of support between the sources using their contents **and** reliability.

How do I answer question 4?

Question 4 will ask you to evaluate either the **utility** or **reliability** of sources using Sources D and E and your own knowledge. These could be written sources such as letters, diaries or a speech, or visual sources such as illustrations, cartoons, photographs or posters.

What is meant by utility?

This means deciding what is useful about each of the sources in studying the particular topic. This could mean:

- What is useful about the contents – the information given by the sources – what they show or suggest compared to your own knowledge of the topic.
- What is useful about the Nature, Origins and/or Purpose of the sources – who wrote them, when and why.
- Whether there are any limitations to the contents and Nature, Origins and/or Purpose of the sources.

What is meant by reliability?

This means deciding how far you can trust the source – believe what it says or shows. You can test reliability by:

- Checking the contents of the source (the information it gives) against what you know about the event. Does it give an accurate view? Has anything been missed out?
- Examining the Nature, Origins and/or Purpose of the source. Can you fully trust who produced the source? Are they giving you a one-sided, exaggerated or even distorted view in order to get your support?

In other words…

You may see an advert for a car either on television or in a newspaper.

The advert would be useful in giving the manufacturer's view of the car. However, it will not be reliable because you may not be able to trust or believe what the manufacturer says about the car because they may exaggerate its good points.

How will I be marked?

This question is worth 10 marks. The mark scheme gives:

- 4–5 marks for judgement of the usefulness/reliability of the contents **or** Nature, Origins and/or Purpose of one of the sources
- 6–7 marks for judgement of the usefulness/reliability of the contents **or** Nature, Origins, and/or Purpose of both of the sources
- 8–10 marks for a judgement of the usefulness/reliability of the contents **and** Nature, Origins and/or Purpose of the sources.

Your answer needs to make a judgement on the usefulness/reliability of the contents **and** Nature, Origins and/or Purpose of both of the sources.

How do I answer question 5?

Question 5 is called the **hypothesis** question. It will ask you about all of the sources in the Sources booklet.

What is meant by the hypothesis question?

Hypothesis means a view of the given event or person. The question will give you a hypothesis to test using the sources. Here is an example from option 3A.

Study all the sources (A to F) and use your own knowledge.

'The main reason for the failure to break through during the Somme offensive was the strong German defences.'

> This is the hypothesis or view.

How far do the sources in this paper support this statement? Use details from the sources and your own knowledge to explain your answer.

> This is what the question is asking you to do.

You will need to consider each of the sources individually and see which side of the argument you would put them on. You are asked to use your own knowledge, but that is not to say whether you agree with the hypothesis. You need to use your contextual knowledge in order to consider whether the sources agree with the hypothesis. Your knowledge will also help you to think about the reliability of the sources.

In other words…

It is like a court case where the jury is given the prosecution evidence (the evidence for) and the defence evidence (evidence against) and has to weigh up the evidence before making a judgement on the person on trial. You have to do the same with the evidence for and the evidence against the hypothesis.

How will I be marked?

This question is worth 16 marks. The mark scheme gives:

- 5–6 marks for a supported answer using only one or two of the sources
- 7–8 marks for a supported answer using three or more of the sources
- 9–10 marks for using the contents and/or reliability of some of the sources to reach a judgement supporting or challenging the hypothesis
- 11–12 marks for using the contents and/or reliability of most of the sources to make a judgement supporting **or** challenging the hypothesis
- 13–14 marks for a fully balanced answer using the contents and/or reliability of the sources to make a judgement supporting **and** challenging the hypothesis
- 15–16 marks for also making a balanced judgement taking into account the strength of the evidence.

You need to use the contents and/or reliability of the sources to make a judgement agreeing **and** disagreeing with the hypothesis. In question 5, there are also 4 marks available for spelling, punctuation and grammar (see the mark scheme on page 84). Take extra care over your writing and try to leave time to check your answer at the end.

OPTION 3A: War and the transformation of British society, c.1903–28

The Somme, 1916

How do I answer question 1?

Source A: A German machine-gunner describes shooting advancing British soldiers on the first day of the Battle of the Somme.

> The officers were in front. I noticed one of them walking calmly carrying a stick. When we started firing, we just had to load and reload. They went down in their hundreds. You didn't have to aim. You just fired into them.

Remember

For this question you are aiming to write two supported inferences. This is explained on page 87.

What can you learn from Source A about the first day of the Battle of the Somme? (6)

Activity 1: Understanding the exam question

What mark would you give the following answers? Give a brief explanation for each decision. You should give:

- 1 mark for copying or summarising the source
- 2 marks for one unsupported inference
- 3 marks for two unsupported inferences
- 4–5 marks for one supported inference.

	Student answer	Mark	Reason
A	When the Germans started firing, the British soldiers went down in their hundreds.		
B	The British officers did not expect to face German machine-gunners because the source says that they were out in front walking calmly carrying a stick.		
C	It was easy for the German machine-gunners.		
D	The source suggests that it was easy for the German machine-gunners because it says that they just had to load and then reload and the British soldiers went down in their hundreds.		

Activity 2: Improving an answer

Here is an answer with one supported and one unsupported inference. Improve the answer with details of how this second inference is supported by the source.

The source suggests that the British suffered very heavy casualties during the attack. This is because it says that 'they went down in their hundreds'.

The source also suggests that the British did not expect any resistance ....

....

How do I answer question 2?

Study Source B and use your own knowledge.
What was the purpose of this film? Use details of the still from the film and your own knowledge to explain your answer.

Remember

For this question you are aiming to identify the purpose of the source and support this with evidence from the source and your own contextual knowledge. This is explained on page 88.

Activity 1: Understanding the exam question

1. This question is worth 8 marks. Using this information, how much would you expect to write in your answer? Ring your choice.
   - Two sentences
   - One paragraph
   - Two paragraphs

2. Approximately how long should you spend answering this question? Ring your choice.
   - 3 minutes
   - 6 minutes
   - 12 minutes

3. What is the question asking you to do? Ring your choice.
   - Explain the purpose of the source
   - Explain how reliable it is
   - Summarise the source

Activity 1: Planning an answer

1. You are going to plan an answer to this question. Complete the boxes opposite to help you work out the message and purpose of the source.

Source B: A still from *The Battle of the Somme,* 1916, showing attacks by British troops. This was an official film made by the British government to be shown to the public.

Who produced the source?

When was it produced?

What details have been included and why?	What do these suggest about the purpose of the film?

What is the centre of attention and how has the photographer made it the centre of attention?	Has anything been deliberately missed out?

Purpose What is the purpose of the source? What was it trying to make people think or do?	**Contextual knowledge** What do you know about the first day of the Somme which might support this purpose?

2. Now write a full answer to the question on a separate piece of paper.

Activity 3: Using the mark scheme

What mark would you give the following answer? Give a reason for your decision.

Level 2	○ 3–4 marks if it identifies the message of the source and supports it with details from the source **or** own knowledge ○ 5 marks if it identifies the message of the source and supports it with details from the source **and** own knowledge
Level 3	○ 6–7 marks if it explains the content, context and purpose of the source, analysing either the selection or treatment of content to explain purpose ○ 8 marks for analysing the selection and treatment of content to explain purpose

The source suggests that the attack was successful. This is shown by various details in the photograph. Most of the advancing British soldiers have managed to cross the barbed wire and are advancing towards the German trenches. There are few casualties shown. In addition, the photograph is a still from a film made by the British government who will want the British public to think that the attack has worked. This film was made at a time when the British were suffering heavy casualties on the Somme.

Mark	Reason

How do I answer question 3?

Source A: A German machine-gunner describes shooting advancing British soldiers on the first day of the Battle of the Somme.

> The officers were in front. I noticed one of them walking calmly carrying a stick. When we started firing, we just had to load and reload. They went down in their hundreds. You didn't have to aim. You just fired into them.

Source B: A still from *The Battle of the Somme,* 1916, showing attacks by British troops. This was an official film made by the British government to be shown to the public.

Remember

For this question you are aiming to cross-reference the sources and identify agreement and disagreement and the extent of support between the sources, using content and reliability. This is explained on page 89.

Source C: An account of a soldier who fought at the Somme. It was given in a television interview many years later.

> The commanding officer said 'You will find the barbed wire in front of the German trenches blown away'. Blown away! Nothing of the sort! It was as solid as anything. That was the whole trouble. Wrong information.

Study Sources A, B and C

How far do Sources A and B support the evidence of Source C about the first day of the Battle of the Somme? Explain your answer using the sources. (10)

Activity 1: Understanding the exam question

1. This question is worth 10 marks. Using this information, how much would you expect to write in your answer? Ring your choice.
   - One paragraph
   - Two paragraphs
   - Three paragraphs

2. Approximately how long should you spend answering this question? Ring your choice.
   - 7 minutes
   - 15 minutes
   - 25 minutes

Activity 2: Build and write an answer

Step 1 Cross-reference Source A with Source C.

○ In blue, highlight in each source any agreement between A and C.

○ In yellow, highlight any disagreement between A and C.

Step 2 Examine the reliability of Sources A and C.

Who wrote the sources, when and why? For example, both are eyewitness accounts. How does this affect agreement or disagreement between the sources? Complete the following planning grid.

	Agreement	Disagreement
Source A		
Source C		

Step 3 Make a judgement.

Make a judgement on the extent of agreement/disagreement between Sources A and C based on contents/reliability. Give a reason for your decision under the relevant heading in the table below.

Strongly agree	Mainly agree	Mainly disagree	Strongly disagree

Step 4 Cross-reference Source B with Source C.

○ In green, highlight in each source any agreement between B and C.

○ In orange, highlight any disagreement between B and C.

Step 5 Examine the reliability of Sources B and C.

Who wrote the sources, when and why? How does this affect agreement or disagreement between the sources? Complete the following planning grid.

	Agreement	Disagreement
Source B		
Source C		

Step 6 Reach a judgement.

Reach a judgement on the extent of agreement/disagreement between Sources B and C based on contents/reliability. Give a reason for your decision under the relevant heading in the table below.

Strongly agree	Mainly agree	Mainly disagree	Strongly disagree

Step 7 Write an answer.

Write an answer to this question on a separate piece of paper. Remember to use phrases such as 'strongly agree', 'strongly disagree', 'some agreement', 'little agreement'.

Activity 3: Using the mark scheme

1. Using the mark scheme below, assess the following student answer. Give a reason for your decision.
2. How would you improve the answer?

Level	
2	○ 4–6 marks for supported statements showing agreement **or** disagreement between the sources ○ 7 marks for supported statements showing agreement **and** disagreement between the sources
3	○ 8–9 marks for a judgement on the degree of support between the sources using their contents **or** reliability ○ 9–10 marks for a judgement on the degree of support between the sources using their contents **and** reliability

Source A agrees with the evidence of Source C because it suggests that the German defences, especially the barbed wire, were still there and the German defences were strong. This is supported by Source A which says that the German machine-gunners stood in the way of the attacking British troops and there were many casualties. Source A also disagrees with Source C as Source A focuses on the effects of the German machine-gunners on the attack and Source C on the problems caused by the barbed wire.

Source B agrees with Source C because Source C mentions the barbed wire and suggests that it had not been destroyed. This can be seen in the foreground of Source B where the barbed wire seems undamaged. However, Source B disagrees with Source C by suggesting that most of the attackers were able to get across the barbed wire.

Mark	Reason	How would you improve it?

Question 4 will ask about either utility or reliability.

Utility

Source D: An account of fighting on the first day of the Battle of the Somme by a British soldier. This was given in an interview in 1968.

> The two of us dived into a hole and began discussing what to do. I came to the conclusion that it would be suicidal to go on and we should stay under cover. However, Lieutenant Wallace said we had orders and we must go on. At this he stood up and within a few seconds dropped down dead, riddled with bullets. Having observed his actions, I stood up and was immediately hit by bullets.

Source E: An official British photograph, early November 1916, showing an area of No-Man's-Land during the Battle of the Somme.

Remember
Utility is explained on page 90.

Study Sources D and E and use your own knowledge.
How useful are Sources D and E as evidence of the Battle of the Somme?
Explain your answer using the sources and your own knowledge. (10)

This question is asking you to make judgements on the usefulness of each source.

Activity 1: Understanding the exam question

1. This question is worth 10 marks. Using this information, how much would you expect to write in your answer? Ring your choice.
   - One paragraph
   - Two paragraphs
   - Three paragraphs

2. Approximately how long should you spend answering this question? Ring your choice.
   - 7 minutes
   - 15 minutes
   - 25 minutes

Activity 2: Build an answer

Step 1 Reach a judgement on what is useful and on the limitations of the <u>contents</u> of Source D.

- What does it suggest about the conditions in No-Man's-Land during the Battle of the Somme?
- How useful is this compared to your own knowledge?
- Are there any limitations in the contents of the source? For example, how typical is the account of the fighting during the Battle of the Somme? Are there any important omissions?

Step 2 Reach judgements on what is useful and the limitations of the Nature, Origins and/or Purpose (NOP) of Source D. Remember, you should be examining:

- when the source was produced
- the person who produced the source
- the type of source
- why it was produced.

However, you do not have to make use of all three in your answer. Decide which are the most appropriate for each source.

Step 3 Repeat Step 1 for Source E.

Step 4 Repeat Step 2 for Source E.

Step 5 Complete the following planning grid.

Source	Usefulness of contents	Limitations of contents	Usefulness of NOP	Limitations of NOP
D				
E				

Reliability

Study Sources D and E and use your own knowledge.
How reliable are Sources D and E as evidence of the Battle of the Somme?
Explain your answer using the sources and your own knowledge. (10)

Remember
Reliability is explained on page 90.

You need to test the information given in the source against your own contextual knowledge, to see whether you can trust what has been written or shown.

Activity 3: Planning an answer on the reliability of Source D

Match the following extracts A–D to the relevant column of the table below.

Extract A

Source D is less reliable because it was written by a soldier who may be giving a one-sided view of the Battle of the Somme because he witnessed the death of an officer and was wounded during the battle. His experiences were limited to the first day and one small area of No-Man's-Land.

Extract B

Source D, however, only provides evidence of one incident in No-Man's-Land. This was not typical of all the attacks on the Somme. In September the creeping barrage meant that some attacks were successful in getting across No-Man's-Land with far fewer casualties.

Extract C

Source D is reliable because it was written by a soldier who served on the Western Front who experienced the conditions at the Somme. The interview was given over fifty years later when the soldier had no reason to exaggerate or distort what happened.

Extract D

Source D is reliable because it suggests that many British soldiers were killed or wounded trying to get across No-Man's-Land. The account gives the example of the officer who stands up and is immediately killed. This was the case, as the attackers, especially on the first day of the Somme, had little or no cover against the German machine-gunners.

	Reliable in content	Reliable in NOP	Unreliable in content	Unreliable in NOP
Source D				

Activity 4: Planning an answer on the reliability of Source E

Now plan an answer on the reliability of Source E. Use a separate piece of paper if necessary.

	Reliable in content	Reliable in NOP	Unreliable in content	Unreliable in NOP
Source E				

How do I answer question 5?

Source F: A British historian writing about the events leading to the Battle of the Somme.

When the British press reported a speech by a member of the government requesting workers in munitions factories not to question why the Whitsun Bank Holiday was being suspended, a German commander commented that it was 'the surest proof that there will be a great British offensive before long'. So the Germans began practising rushing the machine guns from their dugouts to the parapet. Soon they had it perfected to a three-minute drill.

Study all the sources (A to F) and use your own knowledge.

'The main reason for the failure to break through during the Somme offensive was the strong German defences.'

How far do the sources in this paper support this statement? Use details from the sources and your own knowledge to explain your answer. (16)

This question is asking you to make judgements on the hypothesis – the view given – using Source F and the other sources (A–E) which you have already used in questions 1–4.

Remember

Remember that there are up to 4 additional marks available for spelling, punctuation and grammar (see page 104).

Activity 1: Understanding the exam question

1. This question is worth 16 marks. Using this information, how much would you expect to write in your answer? Ring your choice.
   - Two paragraphs
   - Three paragraphs
   - Four paragraphs

2. Approximately how long should you spend answering this question? Ring your choice.
   - 10 minutes
   - 15 minutes
   - 25 minutes

Remember

Question 5 is a hypothesis question. There is more explanation of the hypothesis question on page 91.

Activity 2: Build an answer

Complete the planning grid opposite.

Step 1 Support and challenge

You have already used Sources A–E in questions 1–4, but you will also have to examine Source F.
- Decide which sources support and which sources challenge the hypothesis. Remember that some sources may provide support and challenge.
- Make judgements on the extent of support and challenge given by each source. Use judgement phrases such as *strongly support, strongly challenge, little support*.

Step 2 Reliability

Make judgements on the reliability of the sources in supporting or challenging the hypothesis. For example, if the content of a source strongly supports the hypothesis but it is generally unreliable, then this would weaken its support for the hypothesis. Make a judgement on the reliability of a source on a scale of 1–5, with 5 being very reliable and 1 very unreliable.

Planning grid

Source	Support	Challenge	Extent of support	Reliability 1–5	Extent of challenge
A					
B					
C					
D					
E					
F					

Activity 3: Writing up your answer

You are now ready to write up your answer. Here is a writing grid to help you.

Begin with the sources which support the hypothesis. Remember to make judgements on both their contents and reliability.	
Now explain the sources which challenge the hypothesis. Remember to make judgements on both their contents and reliability.	
You will need a conclusion which makes your final judgement on the hypothesis. Base this on the strength of the evidence in support of and challenging the hypothesis. Remember to base this on the contents and reliability of the sources.	

Activity 4: Using the mark scheme

Level	
2	o 5–6 marks for a supported answer using one or two of the sources o 7–8 marks for a supported answer using three or more of the sources
3	o 9–10 marks for using the contents and/or reliability of some of the sources to reach a judgement supporting or challenging the hypothesis o 11–12 marks for using the contents **and** reliability of the sources to make a judgement supporting **or** challenging the hypothesis
4	o 13–14 marks for a fully balanced answer using the contents and/or reliability of the sources to make a judgement supporting **and** challenging the hypothesis o 15–16 marks for also making a judgement taking into account the strength of the evidence

Using the mark scheme, decide what level and mark you would give the following answer. Explain your decision and how you would improve this answer.

Sources A, C and F support the view that that the strong German defences were the main reason for the failure of the Somme offensives. Source F says that the Germans knew about the British offensive on the Somme because of a speech by a member of the British government which was asking for more volunteers for the munitions factories. The German commander realised that the British were going to launch an attack and decided to strengthen the German defences. By the time the British attacked it took the Germans only three minutes to set up their machine guns. This evidence is strengthened by the reliability of the source. It was written by a British historian who should be giving a balanced account.

Source A provides further evidence of the strong German defences. The German gunner suggests that the British were unable to cross No-Man's-Land because of the German machine-gunners. Again, this evidence is strengthened by its reliability, an account by a German machine-gunner who took part in the offensive. Source C gives further support for the hypothesis. The British soldier mentions the strength of the barbed wire defences and the failure of the British bombardment to destroy this barbed wire. However, this evidence is weakened by its reliability, it was a television interview given many years later by a British soldier who may have exaggerated the situation. It may not have been typical of all the barbed wire defences throughout the Somme area.

Level ....   Mark ....

Reason

How would you improve this answer?

Spelling, punctuation and grammar

In question 5 of Unit 3, the additional marks for spelling, punctuation and grammar are awarded across three levels. These are shown in the mark scheme on page 84.

Now let's look at some examples. Read the extracts below from three student answers to the question on page 101 and:

o circle any spelling mistakes

o underline any errors of punctuation or grammar

o decide what level you think each answer should be in and write it next to the answer.

	Student answer	Level
A	Sources A, C and F support the view that that the strong German defences were the main reason for the failure of the Somme offensives. Source A suggests that the British were unable to cross No-Man's-Land because of the German machine-gunners. This evidence is strengthened by its reliability, an account by a German machine-gunner who took part in the offensive and has no reason to lie. Source C gives further support for the hypothesis. The British soldier mentions the strength of the barbed wire defences and the failure of the British bombardment to destroy this barbed wire. However, this evidence is weakened by it's reliability. It was a TV interview given many years later by a British soldier who may exaggerate the situation which may not have been typical of all the barbed wire defences throughout the Somme area	
B	Source F supports the hypothesis because it says that the Germans new about the British offensive on the somme because of a speech by a member of the British government which was asking for more volunteers for the munitions factories, the German commander realised that the British were going to launch an attack and decided to strengthen the German defences, by the time the British attacked it took the Germans only three minutes to set up they're machine-guns. This evidence is strengthened by the relibiality of the source. It was written by a British historian who will not give a biesed view of the battle. Source C also supports the thesis, the British soldier mentions the strength of the barbed wire defences and the failure of the British bombardment to destroy this barbed wire.	
C	Source A says that the british were unable to cross no mans' land because of the german machine-gunners. this is relible because it is by a German machine-gunner who will not be bieset. In sorce C the british sholdier mentions the strength of the barbed wire difences and the failure of the british bombardment to destroy this barbed wire. this is a TV inteview given many years later and will exagerrate the situation in the somme area. Sorce F says that the Germans new about the British offensive on the somme, decided to strengthen the german defences. This is relible because the riter will not lie.	

OPTION 3B: War and the transformation of British society, c.1931–51

The Blitz, 1940–41

How do I answer question 1?

Source A: From the diary of Christopher Tomalin, 15 September 1940. He was a 28-year-old who lived with his parents in London.

> We can't afford to buy stuff for a 'refuge room'. We have no Anderson Shelter. We must use the pantry under the stairs. One wall is an outside wall and the other is thin board. I am scared by the indiscriminate night bombing of London and the rest of England. It is obvious that the RAF and the anti-aircraft people can't do much about it. We can beat them in daylight, but not when it's dark. How can I, or anyone else, sleep under these conditions?

What can you learn from Source A about the Blitz? (6)

Remember

For this question you are aiming to write two supported inferences. This is explained on page 87.

Activity 1: Understanding the exam question

What mark would you give the following answers? Give a brief explanation for each decision. You should give:

- 1 mark for copying or summarising the source
- 2 marks for one unsupported inference
- 3 marks for two unsupported inferences
- 4–5 marks for one supported inference.

	Student answers	Mark	Reason
A	The source says that they had no Anderson Shelter and had to use the pantry under the stairs.		
B	The source suggests that some civilians were inadequately prepared for the Blitz.		
C	The source suggests that the Blitz was certainly having bad effects on some families because the source says 'How can I, or anyone else, sleep under these conditions?'		
D	The source says that the RAF and the anti-aircraft people could not do much about the bombing.		

Activity 2: Improving an answer

Here is one supported and one unsupported inference. Improve this answer with details of how the second inference is supported by the source.

The source suggests that the Blitz did affect the morale of some people. This is because he says he was scared by the indiscriminate bombing at night. The source also suggests that there was little success in stopping the night-time bombing.

....

How do I answer question 2?

Study Source B and use your own knowledge.

Why was this photograph publicised so widely? Use details of the photograph and your own knowledge to explain your answer. (8)

> **Remember**
>
> For this question you are aiming to identify the purpose of the source and support this with evidence from the source and your own contextual knowledge. This is explained on page 88.

Activity 1: Understanding the exam question

1. This question is worth 8 marks. Using this information, how much would you expect to write in your answer? Ring your choices.
   - Two sentences
   - One paragraph
   - Two paragraphs

2. Approximately how long should you spend answering this question? Ring your choice.
   - 3 minutes
   - 6 minutes
   - 12 minutes

3. What is the question asking you to do? Ring your choice.
   - Explain the purpose of the source
   - Explain how reliable it is
   - Summarise the source

Activity 2: Planning an answer

1. You are going to plan an answer to the question above. Complete the boxes opposite to help you work out the message and purpose of the source.

   Source B: A photograph published in a national newspaper, November 1940. It shows a market stall open for business in London after a bombing raid.

Who produced the source?

When was it produced?

What details have been included and why?	What do these suggest about the purpose of the photograph?

What is the centre of attention and how has the photographer made it the centre of attention?	Has anything been deliberately missed out?

Purpose What is the purpose of the source? What was it trying to make people think or do?	**Contextual knowledge** What do you know about the Blitz which might support this purpose?

2. Now write an answer to the question on a separate piece of paper.

Activity 3: Using the mark scheme

Use the mark scheme below to assess the following answer. Give a reason for your decision.

Level 2	○ 3–4 marks if it identifies the message of the source and supports it with details from the source **or** own knowledge ○ 5 marks if it identifies the message of the source and supports it with details from the source **and** own knowledge
Level 3	○ 6–7 marks if it explains the content, context and purpose of the source analysing either the selection or treatment of content to explain purpose ○ 8 marks for analysing the selection and treatment of content to explain purpose

The source suggests that life is continuing as normal during the Blitz. The message is that morale is still high despite the bombings. I know this because I can see, in the photograph, several people who are smiling. The caption for the photograph says that a market stall is open for business and I can see a woman serving the other people. Although there is much damage shown in the background, people seem to be cheerful and going about their business as normal. The photograph was taken in November 1940 at a time when London was suffering very heavy bombing and people were trying to get on with their life as normal.

Mark	Reason

How do I answer question 3?

Source A: From the diary of Christopher Tomalin, 15 September 1940. He was a 28-year-old who lived with his parents in London.

> We can't afford to buy stuff for a 'refuge room'. We have no Anderson Shelter. We must use the pantry under the stairs. One wall is an outside wall and the other is thin board. I am scared by the indiscriminate night bombing of London and the rest of England. It is obvious that the RAF and the anti-aircraft people can't do much about it. We can beat them in daylight, but not when it's dark. How can I, or anyone else, sleep under these conditions?

Source B: A photograph published in a national newspaper, November 1940. It shows a market stall open for business in London after a bombing raid.

Source C: From an article in the US *New Yorker* magazine, written by an American, Mollie Panter-Downes, who lived in London during the war.

> 14 September 1940
> Hardly anyone has slept at all in the past week. The *Blitzkrieg* continues to be directed against such military objectives as the tired shop girl and the red-eyed clerk. The amazing part of it is the cheerfulness and strength with which people do their jobs under nerve-wracking conditions. Girls take twice as long to get to work and look worn out when they arrive but their faces are nicely made-up and they bring you a cup of tea or sell you a hat as chirpily as ever.

Study Sources A, B and C.

How far do Sources A and B support the evidence of Source C about the Blitz?
Explain your answer using the sources. (10)

> **Remember**
> For this question you are aiming to cross-reference the sources and identify agreement and disagreement and the extent of support between the sources, using content and reliability. This is explained on page 89.

Activity 1: Understanding the exam question

1. This question is worth 10 marks. Using this information, how much would you expect to write in your answer? Ring your choice.
   - One paragraph
   - Two paragraphs
   - Three paragraphs

2. Approximately how long should you spend answering this question? Ring your choice.
   - 7 minutes
   - 15 minutes
   - 25 minutes

Activity 2: Build and write an answer

Step 1 Cross-reference Source A with Source C.
- In blue, highlight in each source any agreement between A and C.
- In yellow, highlight any disagreement between A and C.

Step 2 Examine the reliability of Sources A and C.
Who wrote the sources, when and why? For example, both are eyewitness accounts. How does this affect agreement or disagreement between the sources? Complete the following planning grid.

	Agreement	Disagreement
Source A		
Source C		

Step 3 Make a judgement.
Make a judgement on the extent of agreement/disagreement between Sources A and C, based on contents/reliability. Give a reason for your decision under the relevant heading in the table below.

Strongly agree	Mainly agree	Mainly disagree	Strongly disagree

Step 4 Cross-reference Source B with Source C.
- In green, highlight in each source any agreement between B and C.
- In orange, highlight any disagreement between B and C.

Step 5 Examine the reliability of Sources B and C.
Who wrote the sources, when and why? How does this affect agreement or disagreement between the sources? Complete the following planning grid.

	Agreement	Disagreement
Source B		
Source C		

Step 6 Reach a judgement.

Reach a judgement on the extent of agreement/disagreement between Sources B and C, based on contents/reliability. Give a reason for your decision under the relevant heading in the table below.

Strongly agree	Mainly agree	Mainly disagree	Strongly disagree

Step 7 Write an answer.

Write an answer to this question on a separate piece of paper. Remember to use phrases such as 'strongly agree', 'strongly disagree', 'some agreement', 'little agreement'.

Activity 3: Using the mark scheme

Using the mark scheme assess the following answer. Give a reason for your decision. How would you improve the answer?

Level	
2	○ 4–6 marks for supported statements showing agreement **or** disagreement between the sources ○ 7 marks for supported statements showing agreement **and** disagreement between the sources
3	○ 8–9 marks for a judgement on the degree of support between the sources using their contents **or** reliability ○ 9–10 marks for a judgement on the degree of support between the sources using their contents **and** reliability

Source A agrees with the evidence of Source C because it suggests that hardly anyone has slept over the last week. This is supported by Source A which asks 'how can I, or anyone else, sleep under these conditions?' However, Source A disagrees with Source C because Source A suggests that he was scared and in Source C it mentions the cheerfulness and strength of the people.

Source B agrees with Source C because Source C mentions the cheerfulness with which people do their jobs despite the effects of the Blitz and Source B shows a group of cheerful people who are being served in a market stall which is open for business as usual. Nevertheless, Sources B and C have differences. Source C mentions the negative effects of the Blitz such as lack of sleep and girls taking twice as long to get to work, not shown in Source B.

Mark	Reason	How would you improve it?

How do I answer question 4?

Question 4 will ask about either utility or reliability.

Utility

Source D: From the diary of Pam Ashford, 15 September 1940. She lived in London during the Blitz.

> Earlier this week, I said that people did not seem to be taking the idea of invasion seriously enough. They do now. No one doubts that we will win. The sooner they come, the sooner they will be defeated. Hatred against the Germans is now intense – parachutists and seaborne invaders would get badly beaten up.

Source E: A photograph taken in 1940. It shows a person being rescued from a bomb damaged building.

> **Remember**
> Utility is explained on page 90.

Study Sources D and E and use your own knowledge.

How useful are Sources D and E as evidence of the effects of the Blitz?
Explain your answer using the sources and your own knowledge. (10)

This question is asking you to make judgements on the usefulness of each source.

Activity 1: Understanding the exam question

1. This question is worth 10 marks. Using this information, how much would you expect to write in your answer? Ring your choice.
    o   One paragraph
    o   Two paragraphs
    o   Three paragraphs

2. Approximately how long should you spend answering this question? Ring your choice.
    o   7 minutes
    o   15 minutes
    o   25 minutes

111

Activity 2: Build an answer

Step 1 Reach a judgement on what is useful and on the limitations of the contents of Source D.

- What does it suggest about the effects of the Blitz?
- How useful is this compared to your own knowledge?
- Are there any limitations in the contents of the source? For example, how typical are these reactions compared to your contextual knowledge? Are there any important omissions?

Step 2 Reach judgements on what is useful and the limitations of the Nature, Origins and/or Purpose (NOP) of Source D. Remember, you should be examining:

- when the source was produced
- the person who produced the source
- the type of source
- why it was produced.

However, you do not have to make use of all three in your answer. Decide which are the most appropriate for each source.

Step 3 Repeat Step 1 for Source E.

Step 4 Repeat Step 2 for Source E.

Step 5 Complete the following planning grid.

Source	Usefulness of contents	Limitations of contents	Usefulness of NOP	Limitations of NOP
D				
E				

Reliability

Study Sources D and E and use your own knowledge.

How reliable are Sources D and E as evidence of the effects of the Blitz? Explain your answer using the sources and your own knowledge. (10)

You need to test the information given in the source against your own contextual knowledge, to see whether you can trust what has been written or shown.

Remember
Reliability is explained on page 90.

Activity 3: Planning an answer on the reliability of Source D

Match the following extracts A–D to the relevant column of the table below.

Extract A

> Source D is reliable because it is an extract from the diary of someone who experienced the Blitz and would be giving her genuine thoughts about the effects of the bombing. She would have no reason to exaggerate or distort what happened.

Extract B

> Source D, however, only provides evidence of one reaction to the Blitz. This was not typical of all civilians. For example in the East End of London during the Blitz some people panicked and became angry towards the British government, who did not seem to be doing enough to stop the bomb attacks.

Extract C

> However, the diary entry could be less reliable as we do not know the purpose of the diary. It may not have been simply a private entry and if for publication may give an exaggerated reaction to the bombing to keep up morale.

Extract D

> Source D suggests that the Blitz had made British people even more determined to resist the Germans especially if they invaded. The diary says 'Hatred against the Germans is now intense.' This was certainly the case with many people as being bombed increased their hatred of the enemy.

	Reliable in contents	Reliable in NOP	Unreliable in contents	Unreliable in NOP
Source D				

Activity 4: Planning an answer on the reliability of Source E

Now plan an answer on the reliability of Source E. Use a separate piece of paper if necessary.

	Reliable in contents	Reliable in NOP	Unreliable in contents	Unreliable in NOP
Source E				

How do I answer question 5?

Source F: From a modern world history textbook, published in 2009.

The Blitz certainly disrupted life in the bombed cities. Over 43000 civilians were killed and over two million were made homeless by the bombing. Water, gas and electricity supplies were affected. A survey of Londoners showed that on 12 September 1940, 32% of people got less than four hours' sleep: 31% got none at all. There was also a second evacuation; families were broken up, some for a second time. But the Blitz failed in its main objective. People did not turn against the war in large numbers.

Study all the sources (A to F) and use your own knowledge.

'The Blitz failed to achieve its aims.'
How far do the sources in this paper support this statement?
Use details from the sources and your own knowledge to explain your answer. (16)

This question is asking you to make judgements on the hypothesis – the view given – using Source F and the other sources (A–E) which you have already used in questions 1–4.

Remember

Question 5 is a hypothesis question. There is more explanation of the hypothesis question on page 91.

Remember

Remember that there are up to 4 additional marks available in question 5 for spelling, punctuation and grammar (see page 117).

Activity 1: Understanding the exam question

1. This question is worth 16 marks. Using this information, how much would you expect to write in your answer? Ring your choice.

   - Two paragraphs
   - Three paragraphs
   - Four paragraphs

2. Approximately how long should you spend answering this question? Ring your choice.

   - 10 minutes
   - 15 minutes
   - 25 minutes

Activity 2: Build an answer

Complete the planning grid opposite.

Step 1 Support and challenge

You have already used Sources A–E in questions 1–4, but you will also have to examine Source F.

- Decide which sources support and which sources challenge the hypothesis. Remember that some sources may provide support and challenge.
- Make judgements on the extent of support and challenge given by each source. Use judgement phrases such as *strongly support, strongly challenge, little support*.

Step 2 Reliability

Make judgements on the reliability of the sources in supporting or challenging the hypothesis. For example, if the content of a source strongly supports the hypothesis but it is generally unreliable, then this would weaken its support for the hypothesis. Make a judgement on the reliability of a source on a scale of 1–5, with 5 being very reliable and 1 very unreliable.

Planning grid

Source	Support	Challenge	Extent of support	Reliability 1–5	Extent of challenge
A					
B					
C					
D					
E					
F					

Activity 3: Writing up your answer

You are now ready to write up your answer. Here is a writing grid to help you.

Begin with the sources which support the hypothesis. Remember to make judgements on both their contents and reliability.	
Now explain the sources which challenge the hypothesis. Remember to make judgements on both their contents and reliability.	
You will need a conclusion which makes your final judgement on the hypothesis. Base this on the strength of the evidence in support of and challenging the hypothesis. Remember to base this on the contents and reliability of the sources.	

Activity 4: Using the mark scheme

Level	
2	• 5–6 marks for a supported answer using only one or two of the sources • 7–8 marks for a supported answer using three or more of the sources
3	• 9–10 marks for using the contents and/or reliability of some of the sources to reach a judgement supporting or challenging the hypothesis • 11–12 marks for using the contents **and** reliability of the sources to make a judgement supporting **or** challenging the hypothesis
4	• 13–14 marks for a fully balanced answer using the contents and/or reliability of the sources to make a judgement supporting **and** challenging the hypothesis • 15–16 marks for also making a judgement taking into account the strength of the evidence

Using the mark scheme, decide what level and mark you would give the following answer. Explain your decision and how you would improve this answer.

Sources A, E and F challenge the view that the Blitz failed to achieve its aims. Source F suggests that the Blitz did disrupt everyday life. It mentions that 43,000 people were killed and that there was much damage to water, gas and electricity supplies. It also shows that many people lost sleep during the Blitz with 31% getting no sleep at all. Over two million were made homeless. Moreover, there had to be a second evacuation and a further break up of families. This evidence is strengthened by the reliability of the source. It was written by a British historian who should be giving a balanced account of the Blitz.

Source A also challenges the view. In his diary extract, Christopher Tomalin suggests that the night-time bombing was affecting morale as people were scared and were getting very little sleep. Moreover, he suggests that morale was further affected by the failure of the RAF to prevent the night-time bombing and the lack of protection in some homes from the bombing. He has no Anderson Shelter and has to shelter in the pantry which has thin walls. This evidence is also strengthened by the reliability of the source. It is an extract from a diary entry. He would have no reason to exaggerate or distort the effects of the Blitz. Finally, Source E challenges the view by showing the extent of damage caused by the Blitz with a house completely destroyed. This, however, is less reliable which may affect the strength of the evidence as the photograph may have been selected for propaganda purposes.

Level ....   Mark ....

Reason

How would you improve this answer?

Spelling, punctuation and grammar

In question 5 of Unit 3, the additional marks for spelling, punctuation and grammar are awarded across three levels. These are shown in the mark scheme on page 84.

Now let's look at some examples. Read the extracts below from three student answers to the question on page 114 and:

o circle any spelling mistakes

o underline any errors of punctuation or grammar

o decide what level you think each answer should be in and write it next to the answer.

	Student answer	Level
A	Sources A, E and F challenge the view that the Blitz failed to achieve its aims. Source A challenges the view. In his diary extract, Christopher Tomalin suggests that the night time bombing was affecting morale as people were scared and were getting very little sleep. Moreover, he suggests that morale was further affected by the failure of the RAF to prevent the night time bombing and the lack of protection in some homes from the bombing. He has no Anderson Shelter and has to shelter in the pantry which has thin walls. This evidence is also strengthened by it's reliability. It is an extract from a diary entry. He would have no reason to exaggerate or distort the effects of the Blitz. Source E challenges the view by showing the extent of damage caused by the Blitz with a house completely destroyed, this, however, is less reliable which may affect the strength of the evidence as the photograph may have been selected for propaganda purposes.	
B	Source F suggests that the blitz did disrupt everyday life, it mentions that 43,000 people were killed and that there was much damage to water, gas and electricity supplies. It also shows that many people lost sleep during the blitz with 31% getting no sleep at all. Over two million were made homeless, moreover, they're had to be a second evacution and a further break up of families. This evidence is strengthened by the relibility of the source. It was written by a british historian who should be giving a balanced account of the blitz. Source E shows the extent of damage caused by the blitz with a house completely destroyed, this, however, is less relible which may affect the strength of the evidence as the Photograph may have been selected for propaganda purposes.	
C	Sorce A says he has no anderson shelter and has to shelter in the pantrie which has thin walls. this evidence is realible because it is not biesed. it is an extract from a dairy . he would have no reason to exagerrate the affects of the blitz. Sorce E shows the damage caused by the blitz with a house completely distroyed, this, however, is less relible because it is a Photograph which may be for properganda. Sorce F is by a british historien who wouldn't lie about the blitz, he says that many people lost there sleep.	

OPTION 3C: A divided union? The USA 1945–70

The Civil Rights peace marches of the 1960s

How do I answer question 1?

Source A: From an interview in 1990 with Bayard Rustin, a civil rights worker who helped to organise the march on Washington.

There were about 300 Congressmen there, we had invited them to come. They saw how orderly it was, that there was fantastic determination, that there were all kinds of people there, not just black people. They saw that there was huge support for the Civil Rights Bill. After the March on Washington, when Kennedy met those who had resisted the bill before the march, he made it clear that he was now prepared to put weight behind the bill.

Remember

For this question you are aiming to write two supported inferences. This is explained on page 87.

What can you learn from Source A about the Washington Peace March? (6)

Activity 1: Understanding the exam question

What mark would you give the following answers? Give a brief explanation for each decision. You should give:

- 1 mark for copying or summarising the source
- 2 marks for one unsupported inference
- 3 marks for two unsupported inferences
- 4–5 marks for one supported inference.

	Student answers	Mark	Reason
A	The source says that there were about 300 Congressmen there that had been invited to come.		
B	The source suggests that the Washington Peace March was well-supported.		
C	The source suggests that the Washington Peace March persuaded President Kennedy to introduce the Civil Rights Bill because it says that 'he made it clear that he was now prepared to put weight behind the bill'.		
D	The source says that all kinds of people were there, not just black people.		

Activity 2: Improving an answer

Here is one supported and one unsupported inference. Improve the answer with details of how the second inference is supported by the source.

The source suggests the Washington Peace March was supported by influential people. This is because it says that 300 Congressmen were there. The source also suggests that it was a peaceful march.

....

How do I answer question 2?

Study Source B and use your own knowledge.

Why was this photograph publicised so widely? Use details of the photograph and your own knowledge to explain your answer. (8)

Remember

For this question you are aiming to identify the purpose of the source and support this with evidence from the source and your own contextual knowledge. This is explained on page 88.

Activity 1: Understanding the exam question

1. This question is worth 8 marks. Using this information, how much would you expect to write in your answer? Ring your choice.
   - Two sentences
   - One paragraph
   - Two paragraphs

2. Approximately how long should you spend answering this question? Ring your choice.
   - 3 minutes
   - 6 minutes
   - 12 minutes

3. What is the question asking you to do? Ring your choice.
   - Explain the purpose of the source
   - Explain how reliable it is
   - Summarise the source

Activity 2: Planning an answer

1. You are going to plan an answer to this question. Complete the boxes opposite to help you work out the message and purpose of the source.

Source B: A photograph published in a national newspaper, 29 August 1963. It shows two famous Hollywood actors, Charlton Heston and Marlon Brando, taking part in the Washington Peace March.

Who produced the source?

When was it produced?

What details have been included and why?	What do these suggest about the purpose of the photograph?

What is the centre of attention and how has the photographer made it the centre of attention?	Has anything been deliberately missed out?

Message What is the message of the source? What is it suggesting about the Washington Peace March?	**Purpose** What is it trying to make you think?	**Contextual knowledge** What do you know about the Washington Peace March which might support the message and purpose?

2. Now write an answer to the question on a separate piece of paper.

Activity 3: Using the mark scheme

What mark would you give the following answer? Give a reason for your decision.

Level 2	o 3–4 marks if it identifies the message of the source and supports it with details from the source **or** own knowledge o 5 marks if it identifies the message of the source and supports it with details from the source **and** own knowledge
Level 3	o 6–7 marks if it explains the content, context and purpose of the source analysing either the selection or treatment of content to explain purpose o 8 marks for analysing the selection and treatment of content to explain purpose

The message of the source is that the Washington Peace March was supported by white as well as black people. This is shown in the photograph as most of the people are white rather than black. Moreover, the source suggests that famous Hollywood actors took part in the march including Charlton Heston and Marlon Brando. The photograph shows these two actors talking to one of the black supporters of the march which is to show co-operation between black and white people. I know that 250,000 took part in the march, including a number of famous people such as Bob Dylan, who sang several songs.

Mark	Reason

How do I answer question 3?

Source A: From an interview in 1990 with Bayard Rustin, a civil rights worker who helped to organise the march on Washington.

> There were about 300 Congressmen there, we had invited them to come. They saw how orderly it was, that there was fantastic determination, that there were all kinds of people there, not just black people. They saw that there was huge support for the Civil Rights Bill. After the March on Washington, when Kennedy met those who had resisted the bill before the march, he made it clear that he was now prepared to put weight behind the bill.

Source B: A photograph published in a national newspaper, 29 August 1963. It shows two famous Hollywood actors, Charlton Heston and Marlon Brando, taking part in the Washington Peace March.

Source C: From an article written for a New York magazine, September 1963, by a journalist who travelled from New York to Washington for the march.

> I met a Negro I knew. I asked him why he had come on the march. He said: 'I came out of respect for what my people are doing, not because I believe it will do any good. I thought it would do some good at the beginning, but when the march started to get approval from "Mastah" Kennedy and they starting setting limits on how we had to march, I knew it was going to be a mockery. They were letting the niggers have their day to get all this nonsense out of their system.'

Remember

For this question you are aiming to cross-reference the sources and identify agreement and disagreement and the extent of support between the sources, using content and reliability. This is explained on page 89.

Study Sources A, B and C.

How far do Sources B and C support the evidence of Source A about the Washington Peace March? Explain your answer using the sources. (10)

Activity 1: Understanding the exam question

1. This question is worth 10 marks. Using this information, how much would you expect to write in your answer? Ring your choice.
   - One paragraph
   - Two paragraphs
   - Three paragraphs

2. Approximately how long should you spend answering this question? Ring your choice.
   - 7 minutes
   - 15 minutes
   - 25 minutes

Activity 2: Build and write an answer

Step 1 Cross-reference Source B with Source A.
- In blue, highlight in each source any agreement between B and A.
- In yellow, highlight any disagreement between B and A.

Step 2 Examine the reliability of Sources B and A.
Who wrote the sources, when and why? For example, both are eyewitness accounts. How does this affect agreement or disagreement between the sources? Complete the following planning grid.

	Agreement	Disagreement
Source A		
Source C		

Step 3 Make a judgement.
Make a judgement on the extent of agreement/disagreement between Sources B and A based on contents/reliability. Give a reason for your decision under the relevant heading in the table below.

Strongly agree	Mainly agree	Mainly disagree	Strongly disagree

Step 4 Cross-reference Source C with Source A.
- In orange, highlight in each source any agreement between C and A.
- In green, highlight any disagreement between C and A.

Step 5 Examine the reliability of Sources C and A.
Who wrote the sources, when and why? How does this affect agreement or disagreement between the sources? Complete the following planning grid.

	Agreement	Disagreement
Source A		
Source C		

Step 6 Reach a judgement.

Reach a judgement on the extent of agreement/disagreement between Sources C and A, based on contents/reliability. Give a reason for your decision under the relevant heading in the table below.

Strongly agree	Mainly agree	Mainly disagree	Strongly disagree

Step 7 Write an answer.

Write an answer to this question on a separate piece of paper. Remember to use phrases such as 'strongly agree', 'strongly disagree', 'some agreement', 'little agreement'.

Activity 3: Using the mark scheme

Use the mark scheme below to assess the following student answer. Give a reason for your decision. How would you improve the answer?

Level	
2	○ 4–6 marks for supported statements showing agreement **or** disagreement between the sources ○ 7 marks for supported statements showing agreement **and** disagreement between the sources
3	○ 8–9 marks for a judgement on the degree of support between the sources using their contents **or** reliability ○ 9–10 marks for a judgement on the degree of support between the sources using their contents **and** reliability

Source B does not agree with the evidence of Source A. Source B shows the march was supported by Hollywood actors and Source A suggests it was supported by 300 Congressmen. Source B does not mention the effects of the march. However, Source A says that Kennedy decided to pass the Civil Rights Bill. There is also agreement between Sources B and A. Both suggest there was support from influential people, as Congressmen are mentioned in Source A and famous Hollywood actors in Source B.

Source C disagrees with Source A. Source C suggests that the march would achieve little and was going to be a mockery. Source A suggests it was very successful because it persuaded Kennedy to pass the Civil Rights Bill.

Mark	Reason	How would you improve it?

Utility

Source D: From a letter written by Martin Luther King while he was in prison in Birmingham, Alabama, in 1963.

> Birmingham is probably the most segregated city in the United States. Its ugly record of police brutality is widely known, as is its unjust treatment on Negroes in courts. There have been more unsolved bombings of Negro homes and churches in Birmingham than in any other US city. The purpose of our direct action programme is to create a situation so tense, so full of crisis, that it will force those who refuse to negotiate to do so. We have not made a single gain in civil rights without determined legal and moral pressure.

Source E: A photograph shown in a national newspaper the day after the Birmingham Peace March of 3 May 1963. It shows fire hoses being used against protestors in Birmingham, Alabama. The water pressure was so powerful that it could knock bricks out of a wall.

Remember
Utility is explained on page 90.

Study Sources D and E and use your own knowledge.
How useful are Sources D and E as evidence of the Birmingham Peace March? Explain your answer using the sources and your own knowledge. (10)

This question is asking you to make judgements on the usefulness of each source.

Activity 1: Understanding the exam question

1. This question is worth 10 marks. Using this information, how much would you expect to write in your answer? Ring your choice.
   - One paragraph
   - Two paragraphs
   - Three paragraphs

2. Approximately how long should you spend answering this question? Ring your choice.
   - 7 minutes
   - 15 minutes
   - 25 minutes

Step 1 Reach judgements on the usefulness and the limitations of the contents of Source D.
- What does it suggest about the effects of the Birmingham Peace March?
- How useful is this compared to your own knowledge?
- Are there any limitations in the contents of the source? For example, how typical are these events of what happened at Birmingham? Are there any important omissions?

Step 2 Reach judgements on what is useful and the limitations of the Nature, Origins and/or Purpose (NOP) of Source D. Remember, you should be examining:
- when the source was produced
- the person who produced the source
- the type of source
- why it was produced.

However, you do not have to make use of all three in your answer. Decide which are the most appropriate for each source.

Step 3 Repeat Step 1 for Source E.

Step 4 Repeat Step 2 for Source E.

Step 5 Complete the following planning grid.

Source	Usefulness of contents	Limitations of contents	Usefulness of NOP	Limitations of NOP
D				
E				

Reliability

Study Sources D and E and use your knowledge.

How reliable are Sources D and E as evidence of the Birmingham Peace March? Explain your answer using the sources and your own knowledge. (10)

Remember
Reliability is explained on page 90.

You need to test the information given in the source against your own contextual knowledge, to see whether you can trust what has been written or shown.

Activity 3: Planning an answer on the reliability of Source D

Match the following extracts A–D to the relevant column of the table below.

Extract A

Source D is reliable because it is from a letter written by Martin Luther King while he was in prison in Birmingham and provides his own views on the situation in Birmingham. Moreover, King was the effective leader of the civil rights movement at that time and gives his aims for the direct action programme.

Extract B

Source D is not reliable because Martin Luther King may have exaggerated the extent of racism in Birmingham, including police brutality, beatings and unsolved bombings, in order to win support for his campaign of civil disobedience in Birmingham.

Extract C

Source D is less reliable because this was an open letter written by Martin Luther King, who uses strong language and exaggerates the situation in Birmingham in order to encourage support for the civil rights march and to provoke a violent reaction from the authorities.

Extract D

Source D is reliable because it mentions the examples of police brutality in Birmingham which were encouraged by the police chief, 'Bull' Connor. It also explains the aims of direct action which was to put pressure on the authorities to introduce civil rights. This was typical of the methods used by Martin Luther King.

	Reliable in contents	Reliable in NOP	Unreliable in contents	Unreliable in NOP
Source D				

Activity 4: Planning an answer on the reliability of Source E

Now plan an answer on the reliability of Source E. Use a separate piece of paper if necessary.

	Reliable in contents	Reliable in NOP	Unreliable in contents	Unreliable in NOP
Source E				

How do I answer question 5?

Source F: From a book about the civil rights movement, written in 1996.

> Some members of the movement felt that the Washington March was used by the president to present a prettified image of racial harmony. Malcolm X called it 'Farce on Washington'. Stokely Carmichael of SNCC said it was 'only a cleaned up, middle-class version of the real black movement'. But the size and diversity of the masses, the emotional intensity of the songs and speeches, and the good humour of everyone under the sun, deeply impressed observers. One reporter wrote: 'The sweetness and patience of the crowd may have set a new standard of decency.'

Study all the sources (A to F) and use your own knowledge.

'The Washington Peace March of 1963 was the main reason for progress in civil rights for black Americans in 1963.'

How far do the sources in this paper support this statement? Use details from the sources and your own knowledge to explain your answer. (16)

This is asking you to make judgements on the hypothesis – the view given – using Source F and the other sources (A–E) which you have already used in questions 1–4.

Remember

Question 5 is a hypothesis question. There is more explanation of the hypothesis question on page 91.

Remember

Remember that there are up to 4 additional marks available in question 5 for spelling, punctuation and grammar (see page 130).

Activity 1: Understanding the exam question

1. This question is worth 16 marks. Using this information, how much would you expect to write in your answer? Ring your choice.
   - Two paragraphs
   - Three paragraphs
   - Four paragraphs

2. Approximately how long should you spend answering this question? Ring your choice.
   - 10 minutes
   - 15 minutes
   - 25 minutes

Activity 2: Build an answer

Complete the planning grid opposite.

Step 1 Support and challenge

You have already used Sources A–E in questions 1–4 but you will also have to examine Source F.

- Decide which sources support and which sources challenge the hypothesis. Remember that some sources may provide support and challenge.
- Make judgements on the extent of support and challenge given by each source. Use phrases such as *strongly support, strongly challenge, some support, little support.*

Step 2 Reliability

Make judgements on the reliability of the sources in supporting or challenging the hypothesis. For example, if the content of a source strongly supports the hypothesis but it is generally unreliable, then this would weaken its support for the hypothesis. Make a judgement on the reliability of a source on a scale of 1–5, with 5 being very reliable and 1 very unreliable.

Planning grid

Source	Support	Challenge	Extent of support	Reliability 1–5	Extent of challenge
A					
B					
C					
D					
E					
F					

Activity 3: Writing up your answer

You are now ready to write up your answer. Here is a writing grid to help you.

Begin with the sources which support the hypothesis. Remember to make judgements on both their contents and reliability.	
Now explain the sources which challenge the hypothesis. Remember to make judgements on both their contents and reliability.	
You will need a conclusion which makes your final judgement on the hypothesis. Base this on the strength of the evidence in support of and challenging the hypothesis. Remember to base this on the contents and reliability of the sources.	

Activity 4: Using the mark scheme

Level	
2	• 5–6 marks for a supported answer using only one or two of the sources • 7–8 marks for a supported answer using three or more of the sources
3	• 9–10 marks for using the contents and/or reliability of some of the sources to reach a judgement supporting or challenging the hypothesis • 11–12 marks for using the contents **and** reliability of the sources to make a judgement supporting **or** challenging the hypothesis
4	• 13–14 marks for a fully balanced answer using the contents and/or reliability of the sources to make a judgement supporting **and** challenging the hypothesis • 15–16 marks for also making a judgement taking into account the strength of the evidence

Using the mark scheme, decide what level and mark you would give the following answer. Explain your decision and how you would improve this answer.

Sources A, B and F support the view that the Washington Peace March was the main reason for progress in civil rights. Source A suggests that the Washington Peace March was supported by about 300 Congressmen. It also suggests that it was supported by whites as well as blacks and says that it finally persuaded President Kennedy to pass the Civil Rights Bill because he saw that there was huge support for it. He even told those who were opposed to the bill about his change of heart. This support, however, is weakened by the reliability of the source as it was written by a civil rights supporter who may exaggerate the effects of the march.

Source B also suggests that the march was important. It shows that the Washington Peace March was supported by black and white people. The photograph even suggests that there were more white than black people supporting the march, including two famous Hollywood actors, Marlon Brando and Charlton Heston. They are seen next to and seem very friendly with one of the black marchers. However, again this support is weakened by the reliability of the photograph which may have been used by the newspaper to promote the success of the march.

Source F also suggests that the Washington Peace March was the most important reason. It gives evidence of how the songs and speeches as well as the good humour shown impressed many observers and set 'a new standard of decency'. This support is increased by the reliability of the source. It is a history of the civil rights movement written in 1996 and has the benefit of hindsight and does attempt to give a balanced account.

Level ....   Mark ....

| **Reason** |
| |
| |
| |
| **How would you improve this answer?** |
| |
| |

Spelling, punctuation and grammar

In question 5 of Unit 3, the additional marks for spelling, punctuation and grammar are awarded across three levels. These are shown in the mark scheme on page 84.

Now let's look at some examples. Read the extracts below from three student answers to the question on page 127 and:

- circle any spelling mistakes
- underline any errors of punctuation or grammar
- decide what level you think each answer should be in and write it next to the answer.

	Student answer	Level
A	Sources B and F support the view that the Washington Peace March was the main reason for progress in civil rights. Source B suggests that the march was important. It shows that the Washington Peace March was supported by black and white people. The photograph even suggests that there were more white than black people supporting the march including two famous Hollywood actors, Marlon Brando and Charlton Heston. They are seen next to and seem very friendly with one of the black marchers. However, this support is weakened as the photograph may have been used by the newspaper to promote the success of the march.

Source F also suggests that the Washington Peace March was the most important reason; It gives evidence of how the songs and speeches as well as the good humour shown impressed many observers and set 'a new standard of decency'. This support is increased by the reliability of the source. It is a history of the civil rights movement written in 1996 and has the benefit of hindsight and does attempt to give a balanced account. | |
| B | Source F also suggests that the Washington Peace March was the most important reason. It gives evidence of how the songs and speeches as well as the good humour shown impressed many observers and set 'a new standard of decency'. This support is increased by the relibility of the source, it is a history of the cival rights movement written in 1996 and has the benefit of hindcite and does attempt to give a balanced account. Source A suggests that the Washington Peace March was supported by about 300 congressmen. It also suggests that it was supported by whites as well as blacks and says that it finally persuaded President kennedy to pass the cival rights bill because he saw that there was huge support for the cival rights bill. However it is not very relible because it was written by a supporter of cival rights. | |
| C | Sorce A sugests that the washington peace march was supported by about 300 congressmen. it also says that whites as well as blacks supported it. it says that it pursuaded president kennedy to pass the cival rights bill because he saw that there was huge support for it. it is not very relible because it is biased, it was written by a suporter of cival rights. Sorce B that there were more white than black people supporting the march. their was two famous hollywood actors, marlon brando and charlton Heston at the march. | |

Unit 1

pp 2–3 Activity 1

1. 2 sentences   2. 3 minutes
3. Section 1: Describe one <u>reason</u> why <u>Austria-Hungary</u> seized <u>Bosnia</u> in <u>1908</u>
Causation
Section 2: Describe one <u>decision</u> which was made about <u>Turkey</u> at the <u>Treaty of Sevres</u>.
Consequence
Section 3: Describe one <u>reason</u> why <u>Hitler</u> introduced <u>conscription</u> in <u>1935</u>.
Causation
Section 4: Describe one <u>decision</u> made by <u>the Allies</u> about the war against <u>Germany</u> at the <u>Teheran Conference, 1943.</u>
Causation
Section 5: Describe one <u>reason</u> why the '<u>hotline</u>' between the <u>USA</u> and the <u>Soviet Union</u> was set up.
Causation
Section 6: Describe one <u>reason</u> why the <u>USA boycotted the Moscow Olympic Games, 1980.</u>
Causation

pp 3–6 Activity 2

Section 1	Section 4
2 Supported statement	1 Simple statement
1 Simple statement	2 Supported statement
1 Simple statement	1 Simple statement
2 Supported statement	2 Supported statement
Section 2	Section 5
1 Simple statement	2 Supported statement
2 Supported statement	1 Simple statement
1 Simple statement	1 Simple statement
1 Simple statement	2 Supported statement
Section 3	Section 6
1 Simple statement	1 Simple statement
1 Simple statement	1 Simple statement
2 Supported statement	2 Supported statement
2 Supported statement	1 Simple statement

p. 7 Activity 1

1. 8 minutes
2.
Section 1: Second Moroccan Crisis 1911
Section 2: Assembly and Council of League of Nations
Section 3: Abyssinian Crisis 1935–36
Section 4: Berlin Blockade 1948–49
Section 5: Soviet invasion of Czechoslovakia, 1968
Section 6: INF Treaty 1987

pp 8–11 Activity 2

Section 1
One event of the Moroccan Crisis was the French decision to occupy Morocco in 1911. <u>This was because the ruler of Morocco, the Sultan, … rebel tribesmen.</u>
Another event was the German decision to send a gunboat, called the 'Panther', to the Moroccan port of Agadir. <u>This was because the Kaiser was once again testing the Anglo-French Entente and wanted…occupation of Morocco.</u>
A third event was the British decision to support the French.
C
Section 2
Every country in the League sent a representative to the Assembly. <u>This was because the Assembly was the parliament of the League…appointing temporary members.</u> The Council was a smaller group than the Assembly. <u>This was because it included, at first, only four permanent</u>

members…nine temporary members.
A further feature of the Council was its powers.
B
Section 3
The first key feature was the Italian invasion of Abyssinia in October 1935.
A second key feature was the reaction of the League of Nations which imposed sanctions on Italy which included a ban…Italian trade route.
Then there was the Hoare-Laval Pact. <u>This was an agreement between France and Britain which aimed… invasion.</u>
B
Section 4
Firstly there was Stalin's decision to introduce the blockade. <u>This was because Stalin wanted to force the Allies…Soviet zone of East Germany.</u>
A second key feature of the blockade was the Berlin Airlift.
A third key feature was Stalin's decision to call off the blockade in May 1949. <u>This was because it had not made the Allies… Soviet Union.</u>
A
Section 5
The first event was the Soviet decision to invade Czechoslovakia.
The second event was the reaction of the Czechs. <u>There was little violent resistance, although many Czechs refused to co-operate…April 1969.</u>
The third event was the arrest of Dubček and other leaders. <u>They were taken to Moscow where they were forced to accept…Czech Communist Party.</u>
C
Section 6
Firstly there was the decision to sign it <u>which was taken at the third summit conference in Washington between Gorbachev…respective countries.</u>
A second feature was the agreement over nuclear and conventional missiles.
A third feature was the stringent verification procedures which were introduced. <u>These were introduced to ensure… treaty carried out.</u>

pp 12–13 Activity 1

Section 1	Section 4
✗ ✓ ✓ ✗ ✓	✗ ✓ ✓ ✓ ✗
Section 2	Section 5
✗ ✓ ✗ ✓ ✓	✓ ✗ ✗ ✓ ✓
Section 3	Section 6
✗ ✓ ✗ ✓ ✓	✗ ✓ ✓ ✓ ✗

Unit 2

p. 26 Activity 1

1. 2 sentences   2. 6 minutes
3. Make supported inferences from the source

pp 26–27 Activity 2

A2 B1 C3 D4 E4

p. 27 Activity 3

This is because the source says that the Nazis tried to stop women following fashions.

p. 28 Activity 1

1. 2/3 paragraphs   2. 10 minutes
3. <u>Describe</u> the policies of the Nazi government towards the young in the years 1933-39.
4. Describe what happened

Activity 2

One of Hitler's policies towards the young was to set up the Hitler Youth organisation. He made sure that all boys joined it. The Hitler Youth organisation seemed like good fun to German children, … was an emphasis on fitness with outdoor activities and long walks. Another policy was education which was taken over by the state and used to put across the Nazi message.

4 marks

p. 29 Activity 3

B

p. 30 Activity 1

1. 12 minutes   2. 2/3 paragraphs

Activity 2

A Aim   B Effect   C Effect   D Aim   E Effect   F Aim

p. 32 Activity 4

CA E FD B

p. 33 Activity 1

1. 2/3 paragraphs   2. 12 minutes
3. Explain why the German people disliked the Treaty of Versailles.
4. Explain causation

Activity 2

✗ ✓ ✓ ✗ ✗

p. 34 Activity 3

6 marks

Activity 4

1. B 2. A
3. Second extract would improve the answer because it would turn it into an explanation. The first extract is purely narrative so wouldn't add anything to the answer and the third extract is not developed enough for an explanation.

p. 36 Activity 1

1. 12 minutes   2. 2/3 paragraphs
3. Explain how Hitler was able to overcome opposition to his government in the years 1933-34.
4. Explain how something happened

Activity 2

The Reichstag Fire in February 1933 which Hitler … the communists
The Night of the Long Knives in June 1934 when Hitler removed the SA

p. 38 Activity 1

B, D and E

Activity 2

6 marks
It is one developed explanation

p. 39 Activity 3

1. ✗ ✗ ✓
2. C

p. 40 Activity 1

1. Four or more paragraphs   2. 25 minutes

Activity 2

1. Judgements on the importance of at least three of the factors

2. Hitler's rise to power, 1929–33

p. 42 Activity 4

1. Level 3 because it explains three factors and makes a judgement about one of them
2. First improvement – Explain the fourth scaffolding factor
Second improvement – Make a judgement about the relative importance of at least two of the factors

p. 45 Activity 1

1. Two sentences   2. 6 minutes
3. Make supported inferences from the source

pp 45–6 Activity 2

A2 B1 C2 D4 E1

p. 46 Activity 3

E.g. The source says that Stalin's image was everywhere and there were recordings of his speeches, so they were constantly being shown that he was all-powerful and all-knowing.

p. 47 Activity 1

1. Two/three paragraphs   2. 10 minutes
3. Describe the key features of the Bolshevik Revolution of October 1917.
4. Describe what happened

Activity 2

One key feature was the planning that went into the takeover. Trotsky was made Chairman of the Military Committee and organised the revolution. On 21 October most army units in Petrograd promised to support Trotsky and the Military Revolutionary Committee. Two days later, the soldiers in the main fort of the city agreed to obey the Military Revolutionary Committee.
A second key feature was the actual takeover of Petrograd.

4 marks

p. 48 Activity 3

B

p. 49 Activity 1

1. 12 minutes   2. Two/three paragraphs

Activity 2

A Effect B Aim   C Aim   D Effect E Effect F Aim

p. 51 Activity 4

CA EF D B

p. 52 Activity 1

1. Two/three paragraphs   2. 12 minutes
3. Explain why Stalin became leader of the Soviet Union.
4. Explain causation

Activity 2

✓ ✗ ✓ ✗ ✗

p. 53 Activity 3

6–7 marks

pp 53–4 Activity 4

1. B 2. A
3. B would improve the answer as it would turn it into an explanation. Extract A would not add anything, as it is purely narrative, and C is not developed enough for an explanation.

p. 55 Activity 1

1. 12 minutes   2. Two/three paragraphs
3. Explain how the Bolsheviks overcame opposition to their rule in the years 1917–24.

4. Explain how something happened

Activity 2
The Civil War
The Cheka

p. 57 Activity 1
B, D and E

Activity 2
6 marks because it gives one developed explanation

p. 58 Activity 3
1. C   2. C

p. 59 Activity 1
1. Four or more paragraphs   2. 25 minutes

Activity 2
1. Judgements on the importance of at least three of the factors
2. Reasons for the abdication of the Tsar in 1917

pp 61–2 Activity 4
1. Level 3 because it explains three factors and makes a judgement about one of them
2. Explain the fourth scaffolding factor. Make a judgement about the relative importance of at least two of the factors.

p. 64 Activity 1
1. 2 sentences   2. 6 minutes
3. Make supported inferences from the source

pp 64–5 Activity 2
A 1 B 4 C 4 D 1 E 2

p. 65 Activity 3
This is because the source says that the New Deal offered little to women.

p. 66 Activity 1
1. 2/3 paragraphs   2. 10 minutes
3. Describe the system of mass production used by the Ford Motor Company.
4. Describe what happened

Activity 2
Mass production was about people working in factories. In this system each man had a specific task and stood on a … production was a much more efficient method of manufacturing goods.
4 marks because sound development about production line.

p. 67 Activity 3
B

p. 68 Activity 1
1. 12 minutes   2. 2/3 paragraphs

Activity 2
A Cause B Effect C Effect D Cause E Effect F Cause

p. 70 Activity 4
BE C FD A

p. 71 Activity 1
1. 2/3 paragraphs   2. 12 minutes
3. Explain why organised crime grew in the USA in the 1920s.
4. Explain causation

Activity 2
✓ ✗ ✗ ✓ ✗

pp 72–3 Activity 4
1. B   2. A
3. C would improve the answer as it would turn it into an explanation. A is not developed enough for an explanation and B is purely narrative.

p. 74 Activity 1
1. 12 minutes   2. 2/3 paragraphs
3. Explain how Roosevelt dealt with the problems of the banks in 1933.
4. Explain how something happened

Activity 2
The Emergency Banking Act of 1933
Roosevelt's Fireside Chats

p. 76 Activity 1
B, D and E

p. 77 Activity 3
1. C
2. ✗ ✗ ✓ The third extract would improve the answer because it is an explanation of change. The first is a narrative and would not add to the answer and the second is not developed enough for an explanation.

p. 78 Activity 1
1. Four or more paragraphs   2. 25 minutes

Activity 2
1. Judgements on the importance of at least three of the factors.
2. The roaring twenties

p. 80 Activity 4
Level 3 12 marks

UNIT 3
p. 92 Activity 1
A 1 Copying source
B 5 Supported inference
C 2 Unsupported inference
D 5 Supported inference

Activity 2
Because it says the officer was walking calmly in front carrying a stick.

p. 93 Activity 1
1. 2 paragraphs   2. 12 minutes
3. Explain the purpose of the source

p. 94 Activity 3
5 marks
Reason: Because it has identified the message of the source using details from the source and own knowledge.
I would improve this answer by explaining the purpose of the source using details from the source and own knowledge.

p. 95 Activity 1
1. 2 paragraphs   2. 15 minutes

p. 97 Activity 3
7 marks
Reason: Supported statements showing agreement **and** disagreement between the sources
I would improve this answer by making a judgement on the degree of support between the sources using their contents and reliability

133

p. 98 Activity 1
1. 2 paragraphs   2. 15 minutes

p. 100 Activity 3
D C B A

p. 101 Activity 1
1. 4 paragraphs   2. 25 minutes

p. 103 Activity 4
Level 3 12 marks
Reason: Uses the contents and reliability of the sources to make a judgement supporting or challenging the hypothesis
I would improve this answer by making a fully balanced answer using the contents and reliability of the sources to make a judgement supporting and challenging the hypothesis

p. 105 Activity 1
A 1 Copying source
B 1 Unsupported inference
C 5 Supported inference
D 1 Copying source

Activity 2
This is because the source says that the RAF and the anti-aircraft people can't do much about it.

p. 106 Activity 1
1. 2 paragraphs   2. 12 minutes
3. Explain the purpose of the source

p. 107 Activity 3
5 marks
Reason: Because it has identified the message of the source using details from the source and own knowledge

p. 108 Activity 1
1. 2 paragraphs   2. 15 minutes

p. 110 Activity 3
7 marks
Reason: Supported statements showing agreement **and** disagreement between the sources
I would improve this answer by making a judgement on the degree of support between the sources using their contents and reliability

p. 111 Activity 1
1. 2 paragraphs   2. 15 minutes

p. 113 Activity 3
D A B C

p. 114 Activity 1
1. 4 paragraphs   2. 25 minutes

p. 116 Activity 4
12 marks
Reason: Uses the contents and reliability of the sources to make a judgement supporting or challenging the hypothesis
I would improve this answer by making a fully balanced answer using the contents and reliability of the sources to make a judgement supporting and challenging the hypothesis

p. 118 Activity 1
A 1 Copying source
B 2 Unsupported inference
C 5 Supported inference

D 1 Copying source

Activity 2
This is because the source says they saw how orderly it was.

p. 119 Activity 1
1. 2 paragraphs   2. 12 minutes
3. Explain the purpose of the source

p. 120 Activity 3
5 marks
Reason: Because it has identified the message of the source using details from the source and own knowledge

p. 121 Activity 1
1. 2 paragraphs   2. 15 minutes

p. 123 Activity 3
7 marks
Reason: Supported statements showing agreement **and** disagreement between the sources
I would improve this answer by making a judgement on the degree of support between the sources using their contents and reliability

p. 124 Activity 1
1. 2 paragraphs   2. 15 minutes

p. 126 Activity 3
D A B C

p. 127 Activity 1
1. 4 paragraphs   2. 25 minutes

p. 129 Activity 5
12 marks
Reason: Uses the contents and reliability of the sources to make a judgement supporting or challenging the hypothesis
I would improve this answer by making a fully balanced answer using the contents and reliability of the sources to make a judgement supporting and challenging the hypothesis